My journey AROUND THE WORLD
in a Marvelous Gas Balloon
Koa Koala

This book is dedicated to all Koa Koala's friends —
kiwis, platypuses, wallabys, and people alike — and to the many
girls and boys, both here and abroad, who will enjoy
following his journey around the world.

Around the World with Koa Koala

by Kathryn Jackson
pictures by Benvenuti

GOLDEN PRESS • NEW YORK

Western Publishing Company, Inc.
Racine, Wisconsin

Contents

Text copyright © 1974 by Western Publishing Company, Inc.
Illustrations copyright © 1973 by Editions des Deux Coqs d'Or.
All rights reserved. Printed in the U.S.A. Golden, a Golden Book® and Golden Press® are trademarks of Western Publishing Company, Inc.

Library of Congress Catalog Card Number: 73-78210
Why Spider Lives in Ceilings Text copyright © 1964 by Joyce Cooper Arkhurst
From *The Adventures of Spider* by Joyce Cooper Arkhurst, by permission of Little, Brown, and Company.

For the convenience of the reader, foreign words—except titles and proper names—are marked with a leaf of the eucalyptus tree, and pronunciations and meanings are given on pages 140-141.

Bon Voyage, Koa Koala!

KOA KOALA LIVES IN THE ZOO in Sydney, Australia. And he likes living in the zoo.

But once, in the springtime, Koa Koala had the wanderlust.

He wanted to see the whole, wide world.

So he built himself the most marvelous gas balloon to travel in.

At the bottom, there was a sturdy basket, just the size to hold Koa Koala and all the things he would need on his trip.

Into it, he put his best turtleneck sweater, and his pajama bottoms, and his new, red boots, and his large — and not at all new — green cotton umbrella.

"For rain *or* sun," said Koa Koala.

After some thought, he added a largish bag of eucalyptus leaves (which were his favorite food), and a smallish bag of Australian money, and a handful of plain postcards for writing messages to his friends.

Koa Koala was ready to go.

And at last the great day came!

Koa himself was up at dawn, and all his friends (Wallaby, Platypus, Emu, Kiwi, and people alike) came to see him off.

Mr. Addison, who sold balloons at the zoo, checked the gas to see that Koa's marvelous gas balloon was full enough — yet not too full.

Kiwi examined Koa Koala's cargo to be sure that everything he would need had been stowed away.

"You forgot your pajama tops!" he cried. "And stamps for your postcards!"

"Not to worry," smiled Koa. "I never wear the tops — and as to stamps, I mean to buy them on the way."

"Oh my," said Kiwi. "Stamps from all over the whole assorted wide world!"

So pleased was he that he quite forgot to stow Koa's things in the basket again.

Platypus took care of that, with Wallaby and Emu handing things up to him.

"All A-ok?" asked Roger Moromo (a young friend from the bush) when Koa was aboard.

"A-ok, *and* Roger, Roger," Koa called.

Then, all working together, his friends loosened the ground ropes—and at once the marvelous gas balloon began to rise.

Up, and up, and up it went.

"Bon voyage, Koa Koala!" called his friends. "Be sure to write to us —"

"I will, I will!" said Koa Koala, leaning out so far that his friends feared for his life.

Then, just as Koa sat back, a fair wind took the marvelous gas balloon and swept it high over the city — and out to sea.

Koa Koala was off at last!

Sometimes his balloon sailed above clouds, or mountains, or skyscrapers. Sometimes it sailed low, barely skimming the waves, or meadows, or busy, city streets.

But — high or low — wherever he went, Koa Koala watched and listened so he could tell all his friends in Australia exactly what was going on all over and around the wide, wide world.

On Coral Reefs

On coral reefs
In the Coral Sea,
It's always time
For lunch, or tea,
Or, maybe, a tasty
Between-times snack.

Small fish swim out
But never back —
They're gobbled up
By larger fish
Which make, in turn,
A splendid dish
For the Octopus,
Or the Giant Clam
(Who shuts his jaws
With a giant SLAM!)
Or the quivering
Sea Anemone.

And so it is —
And will always be —
Time for lunch,
Or snack, or tea,
On coral reefs
In the Coral Sea.

Ahoy, the Pacific Queen!

IN THE DARK OF NIGHT, the *Pacific Queen* was nosing her way across the wide ocean.

Soon a swift jet plane flew overhead.

It blinked its lights to say, "Let's race!"

But the *Pacific Queen* hooted back:

"No-o-o-o, thank you,
You're faster by far than I!"

So the jet zoomed off, and the great ship sailed through the night into the days ahead.

As she sailed, she saw the water break at her bow, and foam and boil at her stern.

She saw gulls wheeling over, flying fish skimming the waves, and dolphins leaping.

She saw, too, the fin of a shark
and the tail of a whale
and the sail of a sailfish.

On small, green islands, the *Pacific Queen* saw the beaches ringed with people who had come to see her.

They waved to her, and called, "Hello! Hello! Hello! *Pacific Queen*."

"Hello-o-o!" she hooted back.

At last the *Pacific Queen* made port.

Now by that time, the swift jet plane had crossed the wide ocean a full ten times.

That swift jet plane *was* faster by far than the *Pacific Queen*.

But all the swift jet plane had seen — on all ten voyages — was sky and clouds, and winking lights, and the tiny specks of ships and islands lying far, far below in the faraway, dimpled ocean.

POST CARD

Dear Roger
(and all my Chums),
We (Balloon and I) are
floating over the Fiji Islands.
Lots of palm trees that look
like green feather dusters.
And parrots. And monkeys.
I'm keeping a Log - so
I won't forget a thing I've
seen.
From Koa Koala,
somewhere in Pacific O.
(O. means Ocean)

To Roger Moromo
In-the-Bush,
Australia 77706

The South Pacific/The Fiji Islands 11

Teo and the Luau

ON THE SEVENTH-LARGEST of all the Hawaiian Islands, Teo's family is getting ready for a luau — a great and delicious feast.

Teo's mother and his aunts bustle about cooking the tastiest dishes, and piling the ripest and sweetest fruits on large trays.

Teo's father and uncles are busy, too.

They are roasting the meats — a whole pig *and* a whole cow — over a fire in the roasting pit. How good it smells!

Teo gets hungrier, and hungrier.

"I'm so hungry," he cries at last, "that I could eat the whole pig *and* the whole cow all by myself!"

But it takes time to cook such big roasts. It takes a whole, long Hawaiian day.

So, in the meantime, Teo eats one ripe banana.

He eats two sweet, juicy papayas
    and three chunks of pineapple
        and four chunks of coconut!

"Good," sighs Teo. "That was good!"

Aha, it was *so* good that Teo goes back and eats one banana, two papayas, three chunks of pineapple, and four chunks of coconut again. And yet again!

At last it is nighttime and the roasts are all roasted and ready to eat.

"Come and eat!" calls Teo's mother.

"Yes, Teo!" laughs his father. "Come and eat the whole crisp, roast pig — and the whole roast cow!"

But Teo doesn't come to eat.

Where in the wide world can he be?

All the family rushes off to find Teo.

But Teo's father and mother can't find

him. Nor can his aunts and uncles. Nor can his cousins of all sizes.

It is his sister Liani who finds Teo.

He is sound asleep on the veranda, with his tummy so full of bananas, and papayas, and pineapple, and coconut, that he couldn't eat one tiny bit of roast pig — or roast cow — even if Liani could wake him up. Which she cannot, try as she does.

So she tiptoes away to the table to eat.

And Teo, fat little Teo, sleeps on and on.

But never mind. His family will save some of the good things to eat — both the warm and the cold — for Teo.

He will have his own luau
    tomorrow, when he wakes up
        and feels hungry all over again.

A Narrow Escape

ON THE PRIBILOF ISLANDS in the Bering Sea, great herds of seals make their homes.

The great-shouldered males fight to be the leader of the herd — and to sit, like a king, on the highest of the rocks.

The females care for their pale-furred young seals, teaching them to catch their own tasty fish.

Today, while the young seals are practicing, their mothers swim lazily out to sea. There they float and sun themselves.

But look, something is wrong!

Here comes a man in a motor boat.

Deftly, he cuts one mother seal off from the others. Ducking, diving, and zigzagging, the mother seal tries to escape.

But closer and closer comes the man, with his sharp harpoon held ready to strike.

Then — just at the last moment — a helicopter comes down. Its pilot leans out.

"What do you think you're doing?" he calls to the man. "You know there's a law against hunting female seals in these waters!"

The hunter drops his harpoon and putt- putts quickly back toward the mainland.

And the helicopter follows all the way.

Soon the tired mother seal is pulling herself safely up on the shore. As she does, her mate brings her a fish — and her pale-furred young seal helps her to eat it.

Then she and the young seal curl up together to sleep through the short, summer night of the North.

The great-shouldered male lumbers up to his high rock to guard their sleep.

And all is well again.

The mother seals are safe to have their young, and to raise them to be big and healthy and strong.

And — if all stays well — there will always be great herds of seals making their summer homes on the Pribilof Islands in the Bering Sea.

13

Totem Poles

The totem poles
Beside the bay
Tell tales about
A long-gone day
When men
Fought bears —
And even whales
With their
Bare hands.

Each tale is told
Without a word,
In totems showing
Beast and bird,
Once conquered
In the bravest way
By men
In a much
Braver day.

The Busy Time

In the summertime, Analuk is busy all through the long, long Alaskan day.

If she isn't busy feeding the hungry puppies, she's busy minding her little brother. And when he's asleep on their mother's back, Analuk is busy helping to cook the meals

   or to clean the pots with sand

      or to hang the fish on racks to dry.

At last, when all that work is done, Analuk tiptoes out to the shed to watch her daddy work.

He carves the most wonderful things — small seals and walruses and whales, and sly arctic wolves, and wily bears.

One day, Analuk's daddy carved a hunter.

But the next day, he didn't know what to carve.

So he thought and thought.

Analuk thought and thought, too.

She could think of nothing for her daddy to carve. So she slipped out of the shed and went to look for a good idea in the world around her.

But what do you think?

The very first thing Analuk saw was her mother, holding up a fine fat salmon-fish and smiling.

"Quickly, Analuk!" her mother called. "Get a big pan to cook the fish your uncle has caught!"

Away went Analuk — busy again.

She was so busy that it was the next day before she could slip off to the shed.

There sat her daddy, still trying to think of what he would carve next.

Analuk tiptoed close to him. She leaned up even closer, and whispered in his ear.

"Good, Analuk!" her daddy said. "I will begin that carving at once."

He carved and he carved.

When Analuk's daddy had finished, he had carved a round, fat little Eskimo mother — holding a fat little salmon-fish, and smiling from ear to ear.

Analuk smiled just to see it.

Her daddy smiled, too.

So did the man who bought Analuk's daddy's carvings to sell in the city.

"It will bring a good price," he said.

And so it did.

The price was so good that Analuk's daddy smiled from ear to ear.

"You are a good helper, Analuk," he said.

Now from that time on, Analuk was still a busy little Eskimo. Not minding her little brother, though, or helping her mother.

No. Now Analuk was busy looking for good things for her daddy to carve — and learning how to carve small figures herself.

Analuk was her daddy's helper every single day.

"And that," says Analuk — who certainly seems to be smiling from ear to ear — "is just *exactly* what I always wanted to be."

POST CARD

Imagine, Wallaby
(and all my Chums)—
Alaska isn't cold in summer!
The sun shines all day,
and most of the night.
Things grow very fast.
And big! Cabbages sometimes
weigh 30 pounds.
And one big red strawberry
may just fit in a teacup.
Cross my heart!

From Koa Koala,
near Juneau, I think

8¢. ALASKA

To Wallaby
At the Zoo
Sydney, Australia
11127

The Cranky Time

STEVIE'S MOTHER was having a cranky time.

She said that there were too many mosquitos in Alaska, and not enough neighbors. She said it was too cold in winter, and too muddy in summer, and that *everything* cost too much.

In short, Stevie's mother said that she did not like living in Alaska at all.

That made Stevie feel very sad.

He liked living in Alaska, in their own snug house on their own big and wooded lot. And his daddy liked Alaska, too.

But neither Stevie nor his daddy liked to have their usually very-nice-and-smiling mother looking so frowning and cranky.

So one day, Stevie said, "Tell you what, Dad. Let's get Mother a present for a surprise — maybe that will make her smile."

"It might at that," his daddy said. So they got in their plane and went into town.

They looked at lamps and books, dresses and boots, scarves and perfume, and dishes.

"Nothing there that would *surely* make her smile," said Stevie. His daddy agreed.

But just then, Stevie saw a whole table full of Eskimo carvings. Whales, and seals, and walruses. Sly arctic wolves and wily bears. And a round, fat little Eskimo mother, holding a fat little salmon-fish, and smiling from ear to ear.

"How about that?" asked Stevie.

"It's just the thing!" laughed his daddy. Soon the present was wrapped.

And before long, Stevie and his daddy were back in the kitchen, giving the package to Stevie's mother.

"For me?" she asked, looking both cranky and ashamed-of-being-cranky.

Stevie and his daddy nodded their heads.

And when Stevie's mother opened the package and saw that round, fat little Eskimo mother, holding the fat little salmon-fish, and smiling from ear to ear — she began to smile, too.

"Oh my," she said, hugging Stevie and his daddy. "I just guess I can smile at least as much as an Eskimo mother up in the lonely North!"

Then she put her present on the windowsill and began to cook supper. It was baked salmon-fish. A real Alaskan supper.

And since Stevie's mother was still smiling when she put the platter on the table, it did look as if her cranky time was over.

And so, indeed, it was.

When Stories Began

LONG, LONG AGO — when people knew even less about the world than we do now — they wondered about the ways of earth and sky, of plants and animals, and of people.

And so, they began to make up stories about all these things.

Sometimes the stories were told in pictures on walls, or on bark or animal skins.

Sometimes they were carved on stone, or on brightly painted totem poles.

And sometimes they were told in words by storytellers.

These stories often told of gods who had the power and wisdom to help people and to keep the world and its creatures from making *too* many mistakes.

In Canada, the Indians made up many of these stories — or legends. They were told, year after year after year, around the campfires of Micmacs, Malecites, Passamaquoddies — and many other Indian tribes.

Even today, around campfires in summer, and indoors in the cold wintertime, girls and boys can still listen to these strange and wonderful tales.

The next story in this book is one of them, a legend of the Wabanaki Indians that tells how the Northern Lights began.

The Strongest Boy in the World

IN OLD TIMES, there was a young Indian boy named Sabadis — who was the strongest boy in all the world. Having no father or mother, he lived with his uncle, truly not the kindest of men.

This uncle watched Sabadis lift a huge tree as if it were a twig. He saw the boy move great rocks out of their path as if they were no more than pebbles.

And one day, the uncle told Sabadis that they would travel all over the land.

"People will pay to see your great strength," he said, thinking to grow rich and famous.

But the idea shamed Sabadis.

He begged his uncle not to show him off as if he were a colt with five legs! And when his uncle would not change his mind, the boy ran away.

Now Sabadis was lonesome.

More than anything, he wanted friends.

So, one by one, this boy — the strongest boy in all the world — made friends with two great, strong men. The three traveled everywhere together, and it was usually Sabadis who carried the heaviest load, and did most of the work.

The strongest boy in the world did not even notice that. He was much too happy, thinking that he had friends at last.

But one day, the Great Chief — the god who watches over all Indians — sent a small, odd-looking man to talk to Sabadis.

"Would you like to have a sister?" the odd-looking little man asked.

"I would," said Sabadis.

The small, odd-looking man took him into the forest, where sat a young Indian girl.

"Here is your sister, Sabadis," he said. "She, and only she, is your true friend."

Unfortunately, the strongest boy in the world wasn't listening. All he could do was gaze at his soft-eyed little sister, and feel content.

"Come, Little Sister," he said, "my friends must see you."

He led her to the camp that he and the two strong men had made.

But no one was there.

The men had taken their wigwams, and blankets, and bows and arrows — and all Sabadis's things, as well — and traveled on.

Now the young girl thought that true friends would not do such a thing. Was it friendly to go off, taking her brother's belongings? She was sure it was not!

But Sabadis would not listen.

"Hurry, Little Sister," he said. "We must catch up with my friends. I know they will miss me."

So they hurried on, the strongest boy in all the world and his soft-eyed sister.

By nightfall, they came to the foot of a steep cliff.

At the top, the two strong men had made camp — and hidden all Sabadis's things!

By now, they were greedily eating the bear that he had shot only that morning.

Then suddenly, they heard Sabadis calling to them.

"He has come," they whispered to one another. "We must do away with him, or he will grow up to be stronger than both of us — and do us harm!"

So the two strong men threw a long rope around the trunk of a great tree.

On one end, they tied a huge rock. On the other, they tied a large basket, and this they let down and down to the bottom of the cliff.

"Get in the basket, Sabadis," they called to him, "and we will draw you up to our new camp."

"I'm coming," called the boy, putting one foot in, and raising the other.

But his sister looked at him sadly.

"Don't go," she begged. "For if you do, I fear that you will come to some harm."

Sabadis only laughed.

And, seeing that he was bound to go, his sister bowed her head.

"Then let me go first," she said.

"Yes," said Sabadis. "It's quite safe."

He helped the young girl into the basket.

Now the two strong men, thinking they had Sabadis at last, drew the basket up a little way. Then they pushed the great rock — at the other end of the rope — away from the tree, and over the edge of the cliff.

Down and down it hurtled — crushing the basket and Sabadis's little sister.

The boy cried out in terrible sorrow.

And as he did, the small, odd-looking man appeared again — most suddenly — at his side.

"Bring my sister back to life!" Sabadis cried out.

But the small man shook his head sadly.

"Not in this world," he said, "for this is no place for such as you and her."

Then, seeing the boy's great sorrow, the small man took pity on him. He carried

Sabadis and his sister, basket and all, far off to the North — where no men lived and there was neither greed nor jealous cruelty.

No sooner was the basket set down, than the young Indian girl rose up, alive and well and smiling, and as gentle and soft-eyed as ever!

She and Sabadis lived there ever after, growing up together.

In time, the strongest boy in all the world grew so strong that — when he set an arrow in his bow and let it fly — it flew straight to the sky and to the stars.

And forever after, when the Indians of Canada saw bright, many-colored Northern Lights darting and dancing in the skies, they said, "There — it is Sabadis, the strongest boy in all the world, shooting arrows for his little sister!"

And so — *kespeadooksit* — the story ends.

In California

In CALIFORNIA, a family was getting ready to move to New York City.

The daddy, Mr. Kee, was happy about it. So was the mother, Mrs. Kee.

But Cammie Kee — who was five years old — was not happy to be leaving San Francisco. Not at all.

She liked their apartment, and she liked her daddy's restaurant, which was right downstairs.

Cammie Kee liked the many little shops along her street, all twinkling with lights and filled with trinkets to look at — or buy.

"I like the Fishermen's Wharf, too," Cammie Kee told herself. "And the zoo — those animals will miss me when I don't come to see them. So will the seals away out on the Seal Rocks!"

And what about the cable car that goes ting-a-ling, a-ling up to the top of the hill?

"It will never see me again, either!" thought Cammie Kee, bursting into tears.

"Why, Cammie Kee," said her daddy, hurrying in to her quite bare room. "You're crying — come here and tell me why."

"Yes, do," said her mother.

So Cammie Kee sobbed out all the sad and lonesome things she had been thinking.

Her daddy nodded. He took Cammie Kee on his knee and held her close.

"Yes, Cammie Kee," he said. "You will miss all those friendly things — and so will we. But many new things will come to be your friends."

"There will be a new zoo, and a new park with museums to explore. And," he went on, "there will be the new, big restaurant that your grandfather and uncles and I have bought."

"And, Cammie Kee," said her mother, "there will be our new apartment waiting for us to come, with the dragon rug, and the scarlet chairs, and your own bed and toy box — all right in place."

"They will?" asked Cammie Kee. "Is that where they went? My pillow and my quilt, too?"

"Of course," said Cammie Kee's mother and daddy. "All those things are in New York by now, waiting for us to come."

When she heard that, Cammie Kee stopped crying.

"Let's go!" she said, slipping down from her daddy's knee. "Let's hurry!"

Then she went running in to get her suitcase, which was all packed and ready.

So — Mr. Kee got his suitcase.

And Mrs. Kee got hers.

And away they all went, Mr. Kee and Mrs. Kee and Cammie Kee — to board the train for their long ride from California to their new home in New York City.

ALL ABOARD!

ALL ABOARD!

ALL ABOARD

FOR NEW YORK CITY!

From the Train

High Sierras

No one was there
To make it,
On all that steep,
White hill —
And yet I saw
A snowball there,
It rolled
And rolled, until
It broke in two
From tumbling down
A rocky, snowy
Shelf.
Do you suppose
A snowball could
Just simply —
Make itself?

Fruited Valley

For miles — as far
As I can see —
There's tree on tree
On tree on tree.
Apple and orange
And plum, as well:
I'd like to go
Out there — and smell!

Red Country

New Mexico looks red:
Red earth, red mesas
With scalloped sides
And flat on top;
Red arroyos, cutting
Zigzag through
That bare, red land
Where nothing grows
But tumbleweeds
That dry
And blow away.

Wild Horse, Hello!

One little horse
(Alone and wild and free)
Went galloping
Spider-black against
The white, dry land.
I called to him "Hello!"
And now I wonder
If he knew he had a friend
On the long train
That thundered high and fast
Across the trestle.

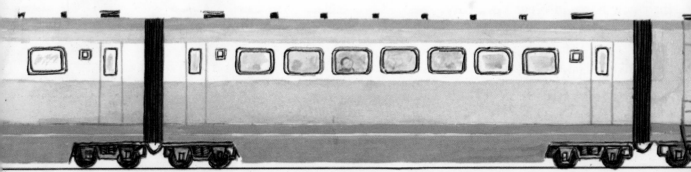

Homestead

*Would it be lonesome
To live in a farmhouse like that,
Miles and miles and miles away
From any other families?
Or would the straggling trees,
Wide sky, and thirsty land
Mean home to you —
And would the thin, brown horses
And squabbling chickens
Be your friends?*

Near Chicago

*Look —
All the land is used
For people now.
Lights cluster
In the towns and cities,
And string along
The busy highways
Where the tame cats' eyes
Of cars and trucks
And buses go peering
Through the night.*

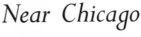

Grain Elevators

*I never saw
The golden wheat they talk about
Rippling across the plains,
I was asleep for all those miles
Of riding through the night.
But once, I did wake up,
And pulling up the shade,
Looked out at bone-white towers
Giant-giant tall beside the tracks.
That's where they keep
The harvested wheat —
In grain elevators.
Did you know that?
I didn't.*

Last Stop, New York!

*So many apartments —
All of them high,
With windows in layers
Going up to the sky!*

*And so many families —
Sitting in chairs,
And eating and sleeping
And saying their prayers
In layers
        and layers
            and layers
                and layers!*

And in New York

THE RIDE FROM CALIFORNIA to New York was a long one. It took three whole days.

Mr. Kee was happy when at last the train pulled into Pennsylvania Station.

So were Mrs. Kee and Cammie Kee.

They were still happier that Grandfather Kee had come to drive them downtown.

And they were happiest of all when he stopped in front of a big, new restaurant that said KEE'S in bright red, yellow, blue, and green lights.

"Here it is!" Grandfather Kee said proudly.

Inside, at a large table, Grandmother Kee — and all the Kee aunts and uncles and cousins — waited to see Cammie Kee for the very first time.

"Now," said Grandmother Kee, when dinner was over, "I shall take you to see your new home."

It was right above the restaurant, and in it were all the Kee's things — the dragon rug, and the scarlet chairs, and Cammie Kee's toy box, and bookcase, and bed.

Cammie Kee was much too happy to say a single word.

In no time at all, with her head on her own pillow and her quilt tucked in, she was fast asleep and smiling, too.

The next day, Mr. Kee, and Mrs. Kee, and Cammie Kee went uptown to the park.

Cammie Kee liked the zoo — which had a pony ride and a llama ride, and some seals so friendly that they came swimming over to say hello.

She liked the Sheep Meadow, where people were flying kites of all kinds, and the pond where there was a boat race going on.

And of course Cammie Kee liked her rides — she had three — on the carousel!

The day after that, Cammie Kee went to the museum to see the dinosaurs, and the sulphur-bottomed whale, and the wild animals, which looked almost alive in their big, glass cases.

She went to a store — three stories high — where only toys and games were sold.

And she went to a tiny park almost hidden among the tall buildings. It had its own plants and a real waterfall, where you could sit in a chair and have a soda with a straw.

And the day after that, which was Sunday, all the Kees went for a boat ride around the whole island of Manhattan.

From the deck, Cammie Kee saw big ships lined up at their wharfs, and small tugboats tooting and taking one very big ship out to sea.

She saw the tallest buildings in the world go sliding past, and far ahead — on a small island — she saw a great statue wearing a crown, and holding a torch high in the air.

"That's the Statue of Liberty, Cammie Kee," said Grandfather Kee. "Many people have looked upon her as they came to their new homes in our country."

"They have?" said Cammie Kee, holding her hat so the wind wouldn't blow it away. "Did the people like their new homes?"

"They must have," said Grandfather Kee. "They stayed. That's why there are so many different kinds of people living in New York."

Cammie Kee looked all around her.

And yes, there were many kinds of people — even on that one boat ride.

There was a lady from India, in a sari.

And one from Africa, with a wonderful turban and a long dress that was more wonderful still.

There was a man wearing a fez.

And there were people speaking Spanish, and French, and German, and other languages that even Grandfather Kee could not tell.

All of them were smiling, and having a splendid time.

"I guess they do like New York, Grandfather," said Cammie Kee. "I guess they like living here almost as much as I do."

By now, the boat had turned around and was heading into the river so that Cammie Kee, and everyone else on the boat ride, could see the rest of the island — which was Cammie Kee's new home.

POST CARD

Dear Chums
(especially Emu),
The Statue of Liberty is just ahead. I'm going to drop this card in her torch- so someone can mail it for me.
After that, we cross the Atlantic O.
(Ocean- I write O. to save space)
With this wind, it should be a fast trip!
From
Koa Koala

10¢ UNITED STATES OF AMERICA

To Emu of the Zoo
Also at the Zoo
Sydney, Australia
12127

The Lonely North

Dead as the moon
And white as moonlight,
The lonely North
Lies frozen in silence
And, endlessly,
In rippled snow.

Blasting all silence,
The white north winds
Shriek in, sweeping away
The shadowy tracks
Of polar bear
And antlered caribou.

Shrill-shrieking still,
The winds sweep on,
Leaving the lonely North
Chalk-white, bone-white,
Dead as the moon
And cold as moonlight.

Slow and Icy Blue

SLOW AND ICY BLUE, a moving cap of ice oozes across the lonely, northern lands.

Strange shapes it makes — ice-blue dribbles and globs, mounds and mountains — as it pushes slowly toward the sea.

Here the ice rises in great icy peaks.

Towering cliffs they seem, as tall as skyscrapers. And slowly, slowly still, this moving ice pushes out into the water.

But look! Some strain or stress is jarring these ice-blue frozen cliffs.

Sudden as thunder, and with a thundering CRACK! one great, jagged chunk of ice breaks away from the cliffs.

SPLASH!

It crashes into the freezing water.

And hiss-s-s! up flies the icy spray.

At first, the great chunk of ice bobbles and bounces wildly.

Then, settling itself, it floats smoothly away from the icebound shore.

So it is that an iceberg is born. Calved by the slow-moving mother ice cap, it floats among the other icebergs in the Arctic seas.

And still the moving ice cap — slow, and ice-blue, and old as the Ice Age — oozes across the lonely, ice-clad, northern lands.

The Wanderer

IN ICELAND, in the wide farm country, one small, white sheep was missing from the flock.

It was Nonni's sheep — the Wanderer.

And Blesi had promised to watch over it while her brother was away at school.

"So," she told herself, "I'd best go and find that Wanderer right away."

She looked in the far pasture.

And in the meadow beyond.

But the Wanderer was nowhere in sight.

So Blesi ran all the way down to the brook at the foot of the hill.

And there she stood — for beyond the brook lay the lonely heath, and the murky marshland, and the stern, gray mountain, brooding to itself.

Blesi's heart began to sink.

But what if Nonni's sheep were out there on the heath, with a sharp-nosed fox trying to catch her?

"Or what," thought Blesi, "if she's wandered into the marsh, and is sinking down in the mud?"

Blesi took a deep breath.

Then, almost before she knew it, she had crossed the brook, hopping carefully from stone to stone.

And there she was — all by herself — out on the lonely heath. Only it didn't look lonely now. It was buzzing with bees, and purple with heather.

But never a small, white sheep, nor a sharp-nosed fox chasing after, did Blesi see.

Along she went to the murky marshland.

No small, white sheep was there, either, struggling in the murky, oozing mud.

Blesi sighed with relief. Skirting the marsh, she went on and on and on — searching and looking for the Wanderer.

Closer and closer loomed the mountain, dark and fearsome, where — Nonni always said — there lived a great clutch of wicked, long-nosed trolls.

Of course Blesi didn't believe that.

Not in the daytime, anyway!

But by now, that mountain was casting a long, dark shadow that said it would soon be night.

"I have to find Nonni's sheep, anyway," Blesi told herself.

And — all by herself — she went closer

and closer to the mountain. When she was almost at its foot, a sudden noise made her jump and shiver inside herself.

That noise could have been the rasping, groaning voices of trolls, warning her away from their mountain.

Or it could — it just could — have been the rasping cry of a lost sheep.

Suddenly, behind a gray rock, Blesi saw a speck of something white.

"Wanderer!" she called. "Is it you?"

At once the speck of white became a patch of white.

Then the patch became a white, wooly sheep coming towards Blesi.

"Baa-a-a!" rasped that sheep — that thoughtless Wanderer.

Blesi wanted to hug her, but that would never do!

So instead, she frowned.

And she shooed the Wanderer across the rocks, around the marsh, through the heath, over the brook, and back up the hill to the home pastures.

It was black night when they came home.

And — can you believe it — no one scolded Blesi, or sent her to bed without supper.

Not this time.

Everyone was too glad to have the two Wanderers — Nonni's sheep *and* Blesi — safe at home again.

When Blesi told about the sharp-nosed foxes that might have chased the Wanderer on the heath, her father nodded his head.

When she spoke of the murky marshland, where Nonni's sheep might have drowned, he nodded again.

But when she spoke of the wicked, long-nosed trolls that could have been lurking in the brooding mountain, her father didn't nod his head.

He shook it impatiently instead.

"Nonsense, Blesi," he said. "The noises in the mountain are made by the volcano that has almost burnt itself out. It has slumbered so long that it will never erupt again!"

"Trolls, indeed!" said Blesi's mother. "Who's been putting that into your head?"

Blesi almost said, "Nonni did."

But just in time, she said, "Well, anyway, Nonni's sheep is safe!"

Her father nodded again.

"You did well to find her all by yourself, Blesi Ericsdottir," he said. "That was done like a true Icelander — for we are all independent people."

Now that made Blesi feel so proud that she ate all of her soup, and two bowls of skyr, without saying a word.

Only when she was snug in bed, with her eiderdown quilt tucked all around her, did she say anything at all.

Then, "Volcano," she said to herself. "Not trolls — just an old, slumbering volcano, grumbling and rumbling to itself!"

And — you may be sure — Nonni would hear about *that* the moment he came home from Reykjavik, to the wide farm country of Iceland!

Go-In-and-Out-the-Windows

IN ICELAND, in the big city of Reykjavik, Nonni is walking slowly from school to his uncle's house.

Uncle Sven and Aunt Rosa are nice — but Nonni doesn't really know them yet. And as for school, well, school is nice, too. But Nonni is new there, and not a single classmate does he know.

"Not one," Nonni says, feeling so homesick that he scowls to left and right.

By now, he is passing a tall, new apartment house. In its playground, small children are playing a singing game.

All of them — except one — are in a big circle, with their clasped hands raised to make windows. That one, a little girl, is IT.

She goes weaving in-and-out-the-windows until — all at once — the singing stops.

Fast as she can, IT stops in front of the boy nearest her in the big circle. They join hands, and weave in-and-out-the-windows until the singing stops again.

Now that girl and boy stop in front of the couple nearest them — and all four join hands to weave in and out. So the game goes, with more and more children going in-and-out-the-windows, until there are no windows left.

Only one small boy, all alone, is left of the big circle the children had made.

For a moment, that lone little boy looks a bit lonely, and scowly, and shy.

"Just the way I was feeling!" Nonni says to himself, and he smiles at the little boy.

"I'm Lars," says the boy, running over to the fence. "Lars Jonsson—who are you?"

"Nonni Ericsson," says Nonni. Before they can say another word, the game starts again.

"Come on, Lars!" the other children call, "we need you to be IT."

"I'm IT!" says Lars, and off he goes.

The game, and the singing, start again. And Nonni finds himself singing, too, as he goes along the street.

"Go in-and-out-the-windows, go-in-and-out-the-windows, go-in-and-out-the-windows, as we have done before!" he sings, very softly — smiling a friendly smile.

And everybody, babies and grown-ups and schoolmates — smiles back at Nonni.

"It's a good game," Nonni says, planning to teach it to Blesi at vacation time.

"And," he adds. "Reykjavik is a good city — it's big, handsome, and friendly, too."

Then into Uncle Sven's steep-roofed house he goes, still singing and smiling. Which makes Aunt Rosa feel sure that Nonni likes being in Reykjavik, after all.

The Brawniest Piper

Oh, the squeal and skirl
Of the bagpipes, oh!
The swing and the fling
Of the kilt,
The rum-tum-tum
Of the slow-march beat,
Oh, the glint of
The dirk's bright hilt!

Oh, when I grow up
And the pipers march,
Look sharp
And you will see, oh,
That the brawniest piper
Of them all,
Is nobody else
But me, oh.

Oh, the squeal and skirl
Of the bagpipes, oh!
The swing and the fling
Of the kilt,
The rum-tum-tum
Of the slow-march beat,
Oh, the glint of
The dirk's bright hilt!

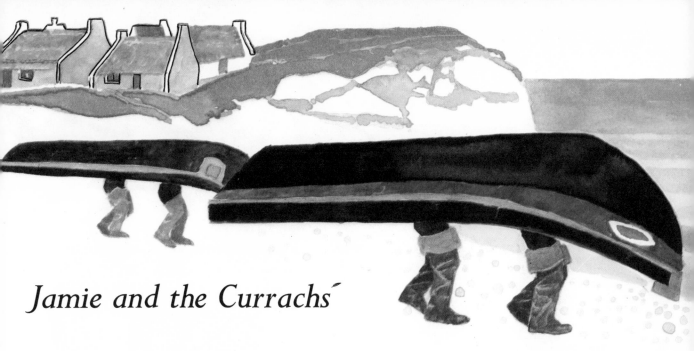

Jamie and the Currachs

IN IRELAND — on the rough West Coast — a small boy was just waking up.

He was in a bed, and a room, that was strange to him — and he wondered why.

Then, rubbing his eyes, the small boy remembered coming here — all alone in a jouncing bus — to visit his Uncle Tim and his new wife.

It had been storming all the way.

But now the rain and wind had stopped.

And the waves, which had slashed and boiled against the rocks only last night, swished softly now at the faraway edge of the wide white beach.

"'Tis a day for a sweater, Jamie," the boy's aunt called. "And hurry, for your Uncle Tim is waiting to make you a fisherman this day."

So the small boy hurried into his clothes and boots. Quickly he pulled his new heavy sweater out of his suitcase and over his head. And quickly — though not too quickly, of course — he ate his breakfast.

Then he ran to the door.

On the wide, white beach below the rocks, two strange, dark shapes were moving slowly, slowly toward the ocean.

Long they were, like great, dark lizards.

And they moved down the sloping beach — each one walking on four strong legs with four clumping, booted feet.

"What creatures are they?" cried Jamie.

"Ay, creatures they do seem to be, the currachs," said his aunt. "But look you now, Jamie, at what they really are —"

And just as she said that, the two dark shapes were lifted up, and turned over.

And then they were only two darkbottomed boats!

Their strong legs were only the legs of the men who had carried them to the shore.

One man was Uncle Tim.

He raised his arm and waved.

Jamie and his aunt waved, too, and laughed as if they could never stop.

But quickly, Jamie took the lunch his aunt had packed, and scrambled down to the beach.

All that livelong day, he rowed with the men and fished in the open ocean.

When the sun was setting, they all rowed back and pulled the currachs ashore.

Again the two dark shapes moved up the beach on strong, booted legs. But now they were not strange creatures to Jamie.

"They're good fishing boats," he said. "I

mean, good currachs — and from ours, we made a fine catch. Didn't we, Uncle Tim?"

"Fine indeed, Jamie," said Uncle Tim. "What's more, the biggest lobster, and the smallest flounder, were caught by you!"

And so it was that as he and his uncle scrambled up the rocks, the village itself seemed no longer strange to Jamie.

His uncle's cottage seemed warm and snug, with a bright fire on the hearth and the kettle singing merrily.

After a supper of lobster, and soda bread, and good hot tea (even for Jamie), the small boy pulled off his heavy sweater and smiled.

"I'm glad I've come all the way from Dublin to visit you, Aunt," he said shyly.

Even more shyly, he said, "I'm glad I'm visiting you, too, Uncle Tim!"

His uncle picked him up for a great hug. "'Tis glad we are to have you, young Jamie," he cried, whirling round and round.

Then Uncle Tim took his cap from its peg and put it on. Away he went then, to visit with the other men of the village.

But Jamie and his aunt washed up the dishes together. They sat by the peat fire, singing the loud, merry songs of Ireland, and then the soft, sad songs.

And presently, the small boy fell sound asleep on the rough, West Coast of Ireland — with his head pillowed gently on his aunt's warm and comfortable lap.

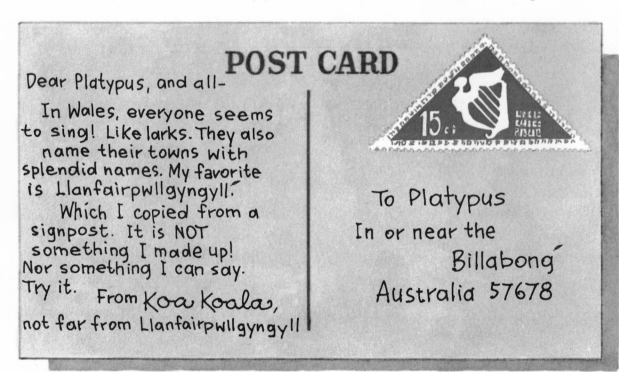

POST CARD

Dear Platypus, and all—

In Wales, everyone seems to sing! Like larks. They also name their towns with splendid names. My favorite is Llanfairpwllgyngyll.

Which I copied from a signpost. It is NOT something I made up! Nor something I can say. Try it.

From Koa Koala, not far from Llanfairpwllgyngyll

To Platypus
In or near the
         Billabong
Australia 57678

15 c

Riding Through the Countryside

RIDING THROUGH THE COUNTRYSIDE, the wide English countryside, the fair English countryside, oh, what will you see?

Lambs in the pasture lands, and sheep in the pasture lands, and cowslips in the pasture lands, and that's what you'll see.

You'll see great oaks a-towering, and great elms a-towering, and neat cottage gardens all set out in a row.

You'll see great clouds a-gathering, and soft rain a-falling, and pop! comes the sun again — and all's washed and new.

You'll see wide plains a-stretching out, lime-green in sunlight, and lo, you'll see dark stones — the tall stones of Stonehenge — darkling and fearsome as they groan by.

You'll see castles and forests, and deer in the forests, and grouse in the forests, and hares in the forests — all fit for a Queen.

And you'll see thick-running hedgerows crowding the roadway, with here-and-there a breakthrough to peep through and see
    Highlands and lowlands,
    Daisy-smocked meadows,
    Children on horseback
      red-cheeked and free,
    Glisten of water
      in snug little harbors,
      on sandy-faced beaches,
      or — glowering and gloaming —
      a-far out at sea.

Riding through the countryside, the wide English countryside, the fair English countryside, there's no end of telling —
    and oh, no way of knowing —
      just *what* you will see!

Let's Not Be Silly, Michael!

IT WAS A BANK HOLIDAY, and Gillian and Michael were to have a treat. Their mother was taking them in to London — to see the Changing of the Guards.

"I suppose you'll play I Spy, too," said their daddy, who was staying home to work in his garden.

He held up a shiny new shilling.

"This will be the prize," he said, "for whoever sees the most interesting thing."

So presently, Gillian and Michael were in the car — each close to a window — and on their way.

Gillian spied a hedgehog, and two rabbits. And Michael — who saw the strangest things — spied a most marvelous gas balloon floating high above the village of Surbiton.

"It was all blue, and yellow, and red," he said. "And in the basket there was something grey and small and jolly that smiled and waved to me!"

"It never!" cried Gillian. "You never saw that, Michael!"

"Did, too," said Michael.

"NOT!" said Gillian.

And their mother, quite out of patience, said, "That's enough! Now let's not be silly,

Michael, or we can go straight back the way we came."

So Michael, feeling it was most unfair, said not another word all the way into London. Nor for a long time after.

Nonetheless, being Michael, he saw some very strange things, indeed.

In Green Park, he saw a bobby looking up, up, up in the sky till his helmet fell off — and into a puddle from a morning shower.

And at Lyon's — finishing his sugar bun while Gillian and Mother went to pay the check — Michael saw a waitress holding a tip and muttering to herself.

"A koala gave it to me," she said. "After he'd had his morning tea. A fuzzy little grey koala — now would you believe that?"

"I would," whispered Michael. "But *they* wouldn't."

Then, with Mother and Gillian, he went hurrying off to Buckingham Palace (where the Queen lives) to see the Changing of the Guards.

There was the sound of splendid music as the Guards-on-duty — all red and gold and proud — came marching out into the courtyard of the palace.

Then presently, the Guards about-to-go-on-duty came marching up the avenue, and past the fountain, and through the tall iron gates of the palace. They formed ranks opposite the Guards-on-duty.

Then came the solemn salute, and then the Guards-on-duty were off duty.

In a slow march — right toe pointing, then left toe pointing — they marched out of the courtyard, and through the gates, and up the avenue to their barracks.

Then, suddenly, it began to rain on the watching crowd. What a hurly-burly! Umbrellas in all colors bloomed as swiftly as mushrooms!

Mother's white one went up.

And Gillian's red one.

But Michael's black umbrella was still neatly rolled and hanging from his arm — while he stood staring at the statue on top of the fountain.

For there, in the rain and the spray, sat a small, grey koala.

It was holding a quite old green umbrella over its head. And it was reading what seemed to be a map of London.

"Michael," said his mother, "whatever are you staring at? Put up your umbrella before you are wet to the skin!"

Up went Michael's black umbrella.

But not a word did Michael say about that jolly little grey koala. No indeed. He did *not* want to hear "Let's not be silly, Michael," again.

So he didn't mention it on the tubes.

Nor at lunch at Fortnum and Mason's.

Nor in Bond Street, where they went to choose a cravat as a surprise for his daddy.

Michael, in fact, was surprisingly quiet all the way home.

When Daddy asked, "Well, how was the holiday in London?" he just said, "Fine."

Then, after Daddy had tried on his new cravat, and finished his tea, he put the shiny new shilling on the table. "Now," he said, "Who saw the most interesting thing today? Gillian?"

Gillian laughed. "I spied a fly," she said. "It was on the nose — of the Captain — of the Queen's Guards. And he never once twitched his nose or *even* sneezed!"

"I should hope not!" said Daddy, laughing, too.

Then he said, "Michael?"

Michael took a deep breath.

And all at once — Let's-not-be-silly, Michael, or no — he was telling about the marvelous gas balloon, and the bobby in Green Park, and the surprised waitress at Lyon's, and the small, grey jolly koala itself.

"And that's true, Dad," said Michael.

"Yes," said his daddy. "Strange but true."

He turned on the wireless.

And there was the news announcer saying that a number of reliable persons (including a waitress at Lyon's, a bobby stationed in Green Park, *and* two Members of Parliament out for a stroll) had reported seeing a most marvelous gas balloon, and/or a small grey koala, with a map and a quite old, green umbrella, leisurely seeing the sights in London before taking off for who-knew-where.

So Daddy gave the shiny new shilling to Michael.

And no one — not Michael's mother, or his sister Gillian, or even his Aunt Jennifer who was a great tease — *ever* said, "Now Michael, let's not be silly!" ever again.

On Rainy Days

IN ENGLAND, on foggy, rainy days, girls and boys play many quiet indoor games.

A favorite one is called Kim.

To play this game, a Leader places ten or so small objects (such as a toy, orange, spoon, safety pin, cookie, eraser, pocket knife, glove, coin, and crayon) on a tray.

When the tray is ready, he shows it to the other players for exactly one minute — then hides it.

Each player prints a list (or draws a picture) of the objects he saw on the tray.

And whoever remembers the greatest number of objects is the winner.

On Sunny Days

AND, WHEN THE SUN SHINES IN ENGLAND, the girls and the boys like to play an outdoor game. Sometimes one called Tig.

One player is Tig.

He chooses someone to chase.

While these two are running, any other player may run in between them.

Tig then tries to catch that player.

And when he does, that girl or boy becomes Tig and chooses a player to chase.

One — two — three,
Rosemary and Rue —
Turnabout, turnabout,
And I choose YOU!

Big Ben

In London Town
On foggy days,
From ten o'clock
Till ten,
You'll hear
The chimes
On every hour —
But you'll NEVER
See Big Ben.

On sunny days
In London Town,
When chimes ring out
Each hour,
Look up —
And you will
SURELY see
Big Ben up in
His tower.

The White Frost

Last night, it was
So bitter cold that,
When the mist blew in —
It froze in icy needles,
Each much smaller
Than a pin.

They gathered on
Rooftops and trees,
And — in a magic trice —
Had set the town a-shimmering,
A spider's web
Of ice!

A Dark and Cozy Time

In Norway, in winter, it CAN be bitter cold. What's more, the sun is up for only a short time each day.

It's dark black outside when boys and girls are eating their breakfast.

It's even dark when they go to school.

By recess time, the sun is up. Then everyone goes out to play in the snow.

At lunchtime, the sun is still up.

But when it's time to go home from school, the winter sun has set again. All in the black dark, the boys and girls go home.

On long, dark afternoons, they can draw or play their favorite games by lamplight.

The evenings are even longer and darker.

Then — when supper is over — the boys and girls hope that someone will tell a story to while away the time.

What story will it be?

Now that is hard to decide, because there are so many stories to choose from.

There are new stories, written and made

into books on the long, dark winter days.

And there are the old stories that were told long ago around the stove, in the long, dark evenings in winter.

Last night, Gudrun chose a story — it was a new one — for her father to read.

Tonight, Olav has asked for a story.

"One from long ago," he says.

Grandfather wants to tell that.

"Listen and you shall hear," he says, as everyone settles down quietly by the fire. Then Grandfather begins the story of Jon and the Three Goats.

And perhaps, if you want to settle down and be as quiet as quiet, someone will read that very same story to you. It is all printed down on this page — so, hush and listen, and you shall hear it, too.

Jon and the Three Goats

HUSH AND LISTEN, and you shall hear the story of Jon and his three goats. Each day the goats fed and skipped on the hillside.

When evening came, Jon fetched them down from the hill, and down the road, and back to his father's quiet farm.

But one evening those frisky goats jumped the fence beside the road. Into a turnip field they went — and there they stayed.

Jon tried his best to coax them out. At last, in despair, he sat down at the roadside and cried as if his heart would break.

Presently, along came a hare.

"Why are you crying?" it asked.

"I'm crying," said Jon, "because I can *not* get my three goats out of the turnip field."

"I'll get the goats out," said the hare.

It tried very hard to push them out, but no amount of pushing could get those goats out of the turnip field. At last the hare sat down beside Jon, and began crying, too.

Now along came a fox.

"Why are you crying?" it asked.

"I'm crying because the boy is crying," said the hare. "And the boy is crying

because he can *not* get his goats out of the turnip field."

"Well, I'll get them out," said the fox. "I'll pull them out!"

The fox pulled and pulled at the goats. But no, pulling would not get them out of the turnip field. So down sat the fox with Jon and the hare. And boo, hoo, hoo! it cried as hard as they.

Before long, along came a wolf.

"Why are you crying?" it asked.

I'm crying because the hare is crying," said the fox, "and the hare is crying because the boy is crying, and the boy is crying because he can *not* get his goats out of the turnip field."

"I'll get them out," said the wolf. "I'll simply chase them out!"

So he chased the goats round and round, and back and forth. But he could not chase them out of the turnip field. At last the wolf sat down with Jon and the hare and the fox, and boo, hoo, hoo! he began crying even harder than they.

After a bit, a tiny bee came flying over the hill and saw them all crying.

"Why are you crying?" it asked.

"I'm crying because the fox is crying," said the wolf. "And the fox is crying because the hare is crying, and the hare is crying because the boy is crying, and the boy is crying because he can *not* get his goats out of the turnip field."

"Crying can do no good," said the tiny bee. "I'll go and get those goats out."

When they heard that, the big wolf, the big fox, the big hare, and the great big boy stopped crying and began to laugh.

"You'll get them out, tiny thing, when we could not? Oh now, that *is* a joke!"

While they were laughing, the bee flew straight into the turnip field. He flew into the ear of the leader of the three goats.

All he said was, "Buzz-z-z-z-z-z!"

But the leader, fearing to be stung, at once jumped out of the turnip field.

And at that — leap, trot, and jump — the other goats came out, as quickly as he! So presently, all three goats were following Jon back to his father's quiet farm, and staying close at his heels.

And so this story ends.

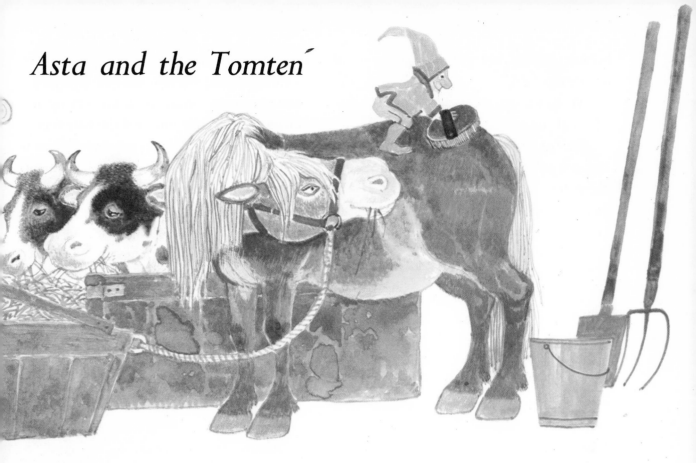

Asta and the Tomten

Now Asta — LIKE EVERY GIRL AND BOY in Sweden — had heard of the tomten. She knew that he was a very small gray man with a long gray beard and a tall gray cap, pointed at the top.

And she knew that it was the tomten who took special care of animals — the cows, horses, sheep, and chickens — seeing that they were fed, and warm, and safe from prowling creatures that might harm them.

All that, Asta knew. She had heard it over and over at Christmas.

But Asta had never seen the tomten who was said to live at her Uncle Sven's farm. So, one year, on the way to the farm for the long Swedish Christmas, she made up her mind to see the tomten that very Christmas Eve.

Of course, she had to wait until after supper, and until after everyone had sung the carols and danced — hand in hand — around the tall, shining Christmas tree.

But after that, while the grown-ups were catching their breath and then laughing and talking about grown-up things, Asta put on her warm clothes and went outdoors.

She went straight to the barn, carrying a small bowl of rice porridge for the tomten's Christmas treat.

And as she went, she looked left and right, but never a glimpse of the tomten did Asta see. Certainly not.

For, lo and behold! That small gray man was tiptoeing silently behind her.

He stopped at the wheat sheaf, set out for the birds on top of a tall pole in the barnyard.

Most of the grains were already eaten, and off he went on silent feet to get another sheaf of wheat for the birds to eat in the morning.

So, of course, when Asta put down the bowl of rice porridge in the barn and called *God Jul* to the tomten — no tomten was there to answer her.

Only the cows were there sleeping, and the rough-coated plowhorses, and the sheep in their tangled coats of creamy wool.

"Perhaps," thought Asta, "the tomten is in the chicken house wishing the hens and roosters *God Jul*, and making sure they're all right."

But when she peeped in the chicken house, no small gray man with a long gray beard and a pointed hat did she see.

Certainly not.

For by now, the tomten had slipped silently into the barn. There he was busily asking the animals how they fared, and — with his deft, gray fingers — currying the horses to a marvelous sheen, and combing the sheep until not a tangle or burr was left in their woolly coats.

He saw the rice porridge that Asta had left for him, and he smacked his lips.

But not a taste would the tomten take until he had taken care of *all* the animals. He scolded the cat for scaring the mice,

and drew a thorn from the sheepdog's paw, and chatted a bit with his friend the owl.

Then he wished all the barn animals *God Jul* and slipped off to the chicken house on silent feet.

But by now, Asta had grown sleepy waiting for the tomten to come to the chicken house! She was on her way to the wheat sheaf which — lo and behold! was a fresh new one.

Asta stopped and stood still in wonder that the tomten — that small gray man — could work so quickly and so silently.

And while she stood there looking like a small, dark shadow against the snow, a smaller, darker shadow was slipping into the chicken house to see how the hens and roosters fared.

All was well there. With their heads under their wings, the hens and roosters were fast asleep and dreaming their feathered dreams.

"*God Jul,* my friends," whispered the tomten on Uncle Sven's farm. And now that all this night's work was done, he tripped back to the barn to feast on his Christmas treat of good rice porridge.

It was so good that there were two pink spots on the tomten's gray cheeks as he climbed the ladder to his snug bed in the hayloft.

Almost at once, he was fast asleep.

So it was that when Asta — almost dizzy with sleepiness — came back to the barn for one last look for the tomten, no small gray man with a long gray beard, and a hat that was pointed at the top was anywhere in sight.

But lo and behold!

The porridge bowl was empty — not a grain of rice, nor a raisin or almond, or lick of milk was left in the bottom.

So Asta, sleepy as she was, knew that without a doubt the tomten had been there.

Off she went, a small dark shadow against the snow, to tumble into bed and dream her Christmas dreams through the long night.

And ever after — wherever Asta was at Christmas time — she always put out a small bowl of rice porridge for the tomten of that place, just as her mother
and her grandmother
and her great-grandmother
had done before her.

POST CARD

SVERIGE
GOD JULE

Dear Chums, one and all,
   Merry Christmas, or as we say in Sweden- God Jul! Ran out of eucalyptus leaves over Oslo. But stocked up with dried fish and cheese from the markets there. And dined on rice porridge, which a fine, gray chap named Tomten most kindly shared with me!
                  Koa Koala

To all my Chums
c/o the Postmaster
Perth, Australia 23254

PLEASE PASS CARD ON!

The Old One's Reindeer

THE OLD ONE, MRS. PINTHA, was as proud and stubborn as any Lapp could be.

But she was Niilo's friend.

Every evening, when his small herd of reindeer was safely bedded down for the night, he went skiing over to see her.

Often, when he came to her tent, Niilo heard the Old One singing sadly to herself.

Voia, voia, nana, nana, went her song, *very sleek, very fleet are the reindeer.*

Voia, voia, nana, nana, food they are, and milk and shelter, for the Lapps.

Voia, voia, nana, nana, reindeer are my fortune, and fortune for my son.

Voia, voia, nana, nana, how shall I keep our reindeer safe

Until he comes home?

"I could help you, Mrs. Pintha," Niilo always said. "I could herd your reindeer!"

But the Old One only shook her head.

"Why not?" asked Niilo. "I do know how, for I have reindeer of my own."

"How many, Niilo?" the Old One asked with a sly smile.

"I cannot tell you," said Niilo, blushing so that his ears grew hot under his cap.

"No, you cannot," sighed the Old One. "No Lapp may tell the number of his herd."

"It is a secret within the family," Niilo agreed. "One that no one else may know."

"And that being so," said Old Mrs. Pintha, "how can you herd my reindeer — not knowing how many are in the herd?"

"It seems I cannot," Niilo always said.

But he kept trying to find a way.

He tried in the daytime while he was in the woods with his own reindeer.

He tried at night, snug under his reindeer robes in his father's smoky tent.

And he tried in the morning, when he awoke.

At last — with all that trying — Niilo thought of a way. On went his clothes. On went his warm reindeer boots, and his skis.

And away went Niilo, skimming across the snow all the way to the Old One's tent.

"If I were your grandson, Mrs. Pintha,"

Lapland 47

he cried, "*then* could you tell me the number of reindeer in your herd?"

"I could," said the Old One.

"Then, Mrs. Pintha," said Niilo, "could you perhaps take me as your grandson — just until your son Risto comes home from the university?"

The Old One squinted her eyes.

She chewed at her lip.

She thought and thought.

"I could," she said at last. "For you are already my grandson in my heart."

Niilo sighed with relief.

"I thank you for that, Grandmother Pintha," he said.

"And now, Grandson of my Heart," the Old One grinned, "how many reindeer are in your herd?"

Niilo looked all around to be sure that no one was listening. Then he whispered the number — a very small number, for he was still very young — in the Old One's ear.

"A fine start, Grandson of my Heart," she said. "Now in my herd, I have —"

Softly, she whispered the number in Niilo's ear. And a very great number it was, too — for old Mrs. Pintha was very old.

"So many, Grandmother Pintha!" said Niilo. "I must go and find them at once —"

"No," old Mrs. Pintha said stubbornly. "First we must make a bargain. Each year, you must have one reindeer from my herd to add to yours. Otherwise, you may not do my work."

"It's a bargain, Grandmother Pintha," said Niilo. "One reindeer each year until your son Risto comes home."

The Old One smiled, and sat down in her tent to embroider — and take her ease.

Then away went Niilo, to the forest to see that not one of the Old One's reindeer —

or of his own — should get lost, or be harmed by the wolves of the north of Finland.

As he went, he could hear the Old One singing to herself again.

And this time, the words and the tune of her reindeer song were happy ones:

*Voia, voia, nana, nana, very sleek,
very beautiful are the reindeer.*

*Voia, voia, nana, nana, in the woods,
they feed on mosses and lichen.*

*Voia, voia, nana, nana, no wolves
will harm them, nor will they stray away.*

*Voia, voia, nana, nana, herded they are
by the Young One who keeps their number
Secret unto his heart!*

Loop the Reindeer

YOUNG CHILDREN IN LAPLAND play a game that helps them learn to handle reindeer.

They stand a forked branch firmly in the deep snow. Then using ropes with nooses at one end, they take turns trying to lasso the "reindeer's antlers."

Anyone who misses is out of the game.

They watch and cheer the winner — the player who stays longest in the game.

Tivoli Remembered

IN DENMARK, on a long, dark winter night, Kurt and Ole and Mette were whispering in their beds.

They were remembering spring, which would soon be coming back to melt the snow and coax the grass and flowers out of the soil.

They were remembering taking off their winter clothes, and running outdoors barefoot and free.

Best of all, they were remembering Tivoli Gardens — which always opens when spring has come to Copenhagen.

"Remember the main gate," whispered Kurt, "all sparkling with tiny lights?"

"Yes," whispered Ole. "Oh yes! And the Chinese Theater, and the pantomime —"

"And the rides!" whispered Mette, who was remembering the mini trains, and the antique autos that you can drive yourself, and the carnival rides that spin and whirl and take your breath away.

"Yes, the rides," Kurt whispered. "And the fountains everywhere, and the playground."

"And the food!" said Ole, so busy remembering that he quite forgot to whisper. "Do you remember the wonderful food?"

"I remember," said Mette, sitting up in her bed with round, excited eyes.

"And," cried Kurt, "do you remember the Boy Guards in scarlet jackets — parading everywhere to their own, loud band —"

"— that goes oompa-oompa-oompa, ta-rum, ta-rum, ta-rum!" shouted Ole, jumping out of his bed and marching up the hall.

In a moment, Mette was marching behind Ole, and Kurt was marching behind Mette.

"Oompa, oompa, oompa! Ta-rum, ta-rum, ta-rum!" they all went, stamping their feet and making the most wonderful racket.

But in two moments, their father came bounding up the stairs, holding his ears.

"What's going on up here?" he growled.

Everyone stopped shouting and marching, and stood red-cheeked and stock still.

And, in the sudden silence, Mette said, "We were only remembering Tivoli Gar-

dens when it opens in the spring. That's all."

"Humnn," said their father, smiling a little. "I remember it, too."

"But I also remember," he said, growling again and looking quite fierce, "the good old days when girls and boys went quietly to sleep when they were sent to bed on a winter night! Do you remember that?"

"Yes, we do," said Kurt and Ole and Mette, running back to their beds and jumping in.

Then thump, thump, thump, went their father's boots going down the stairs. Presently the house was as quiet as the last few snowflakes falling outside.

That was because, away down in the kitchen, Father was sipping his coffee and talking ever so softly with the children's mother.

And upstairs, until they fell asleep that late winter night in Denmark, Kurt and Ole and Mette remembered the wonderful Tivoli Gardens very, very quietly — seeing all its splendor behind their tight-shut eyes.

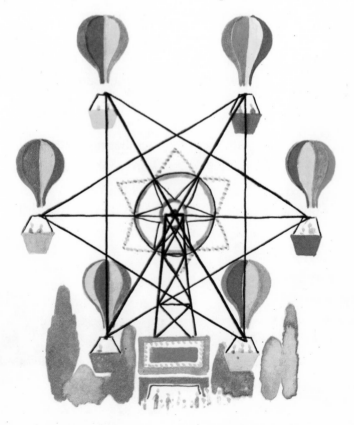

Over the North Sea

ANYONE — JET PILOT, PIGEON, OR KOALA — flying over the North Sea one particular day in late March was sure to see wild sights and brave deeds in the Netherlands.

For it was then that there was a great storm. The waves rose high and gray. They lashed themselves, wave after wave after wave, against the dikes so strongly built round the lowlands.

At last, the dikes crumbled and gave way.

"Hurry!" cried the men on the neat farms and in the trim and tidy towns.

Knee-deep or waist-deep in water, they fought to save their land from the floods.

They thrust sand bags against the crumbling dikes.

They loosed cows from the barns, to find their own way to higher ground. They emptied shops of goods, and took them to higher floors where the water might not reach.

"Hurry! Hurry!" cried the women in their homes.

With their children behind them, they rushed upstairs and down trying to save all their household goods from the rising water.

But even so, cars and cattle, cupboards and caps, chairs and cheese, and even crates of fine Dutch tulip bulbs, went floating down the canals — or sweeping out to sea!

At last and at last the storm ended.

The waters crept off as if in shame.

At once, the people of the Netherlands set to work to repair the dikes, wring the salt sea out of their polders, bring their belongings home again, and clean away the clinging mud.

Day after day, a great sorting and scouring and polishing went on.

And one day, with a bright sun in a clear, blue sky, the farmers' polders were neat and growing again, and the towns of the Netherlands were once more tidy and trim — and spotless.

"Till next time," said the weary women.

"Till next time," said the gray-tired men.

"Till next time," said the children, putting on their sabots so they could run and play on the muddy tops of the dikes.

And high above, anyone — jet pilot or pigeon *or* koala — flying over on that particular day — marveled greatly at the brave deeds and faces of the men and women and children of the low-lying Netherlands.

Ice is Nice!

In winter, when
Canals were icy,
We skated everywhere:
To school, to visit,
And into town,
And — fast as fast —
Were there!

But now spring's here,
We have to walk.
Along the streets we go,
All high above
The wet canals —
And walking seems
So slow!

The Quiet Little Girl

IN THE CITY OF AMSTERDAM, there lived a very quiet little girl.

Her name was Kaatie Vandermeer. And her two elderly aunts — who were raising her — never tired of praising her.

"Such a soft voice," they said. "Such quiet ways! You never know Kaatie is around!"

Then they would give Kaatie a fond smile, or a cup of good Dutch chocolate, or a whole kwartze to spend on herself.

That was fine. The quiet little girl liked it — but not everything was so fine.

At school, when Kaatie put up her hand to answer a question — no one could hear a single thing she said.

"Speak up," her teacher always said.

Then her classmates giggled. And Kaatie wished she had not put up her hand at all.

On the playground, things were even worse for her.

Kaatie was so quiet that no one knew she was around. So, of course, no one ever did choose her to be on a team.

Worse still, when Kaatie Vandermeer went to **van Leeuw's** shop to spend her kwartzes, the shopkeeper never noticed that she was there.

Vrouw **van Leeuw** waited on girls and boys who had come in before her, and those who had come in after her, and those who kept right on coming into the shop.

Out they all went, with their new bubble-pipes or skip ropes or games, or with their cheeks full of hopjes — which are the most delicious squares of chewy toffee.

And there stood Kaatie, that quiet little girl, still waiting to be waited on. One day, she had had quite enough of that!

By now, Kaatie had ten whole kwartzes to spend on doll clothes, a book about circus animals, and a really big bag of hopjes.

"And I will, too!" she told herself.

So into **van Leeuw's** shop she went. She waited, quietly as ever, until everyone who

had come in before her had been waited on.

But when Vrouw van Leeuw began to wait on Cornelia Vurst — who had just come in — Kaatie took a deep breath.

"It's my turn, Vrouw van Leeuw," she said in a loud and firm voice. "I'm next!"

Vrouw van Leeuw gave a jump.

She looked right straight at Kaatie.

"Well, goodness," she said. "Don't get so excited — all you needed was to speak up!"

"Yes," said Kaatie. "And so I have!"

In two minutes, Kaatie had bought all the things she had wanted to buy.

"Thank you, Vrouw van Leeuw," she said quietly. And out of the shop she went, with *her* cheeks full of hopjes, at last.

Word spread all over the neighborhood!

Her aunts could not believe it, for Kaatie was still a quiet little girl with them.

But her teacher believed it, for now Kaatie spoke up — loud and clear.

On the playground, she was just as noisy and merry as anyone else, too.

"I choose Kaatie for my team!" her friends soon found themselves saying.

And as for Kaatie Vandermeer, well — that quiet little girl couldn't believe her good luck, ever since she had learned to speak up when that was what she needed to do.

Stork's Nest in the Chimney

"A stork's nest in the chimney
Can bring me good luck,"
Said crafty Vrouw Maarden of Marken.
"When tourists come flocking
To see it, they'll buy — before
All my wares fade or darken!"

So she climbed to her rooftop
By light of the moon,
With a basket of suet and bread
To hang in her chimney and lure
A stork there. "It may!"
Is all Vrouw Maarden said.

And, first thing next morning,
Her neighbors exclaimed,
"Oh look now, oh see now, oh harken!
A stork's in your chimney —
It's building a nest — you lucky
Vrouw Maarden of Marken!"

Berlin Morning

When Father goes shopping,
We go when we can,
For maybe — just maybe —
He'll buy marzipan.

And we'll choose the shapes
With their sugary tops:
Small pears, and strawberries,
And roasts, and pork chops,
And strings of fat sausage —
There's no way to stop,
Until Father insists,
In that marzipan shop!

When Father goes shopping,
We go when we may,
And maybe — just maybe —
He'll take us today.

Afternoon

It was just a wall
Where we played ball sometimes.
And then, one day, we saw Frau Ada
Waving across it to an old man —
Lonely on the other side.

Now we wave, too,
And talk to him most every day.
Frau Ada says that he can't hear the words,
But thoughts, she says, can cross the wall
As swift and free as birds.

And Night

Listen! The music
Is starting again
In the hall at the end
Of the street —
They're twirling and whirling
And bouncing again
To a tune with a gay
Polka beat!

Lights are all shining
And skirts are a-whirl,
There's the clapping and
Laughing of friends —
It's like hearing a story,
And trying — again —
To stay wide awake
Till it ends!

ONE MORNING, IN A SMALL TOWN in Germany, a little tailor sat at his open window cutting and sewing his cloth.

Buzz, buzz, buzz went an army of flies swarming over a slice of bread and jam he had been nibbling between stitches.

"Enough!" cried the little tailor at last.

Taking a strip of cloth, he lashed out at his tormentors — killing seven at one blow.

"Aha," the little tailor cried, pushing out his chest, "this is quite a feat!"

At once he made himself a belt on which he stitched the words:

SEVEN AT ONE BLOW.

His customers were amazed, thinking that the legend meant that he had killed seven evil men (instead of flies) at one blow.

Their praise soon went to the little tailor's head. The town became too small for such a hero as he! So off he went to seek a great fortune in the king's service.

For food on his journey, he put a round cheese in one pocket. Then, finding a weary young bird in his path, he tucked it into his other pocket so that it might rest.

The little tailor had not gone far when he met up with a terrible giant who read the legend stitched on his new belt.

"Seven at one blow!" the giant exclaimed. "Well, little tailor, come and match your strength with mine!"

Then, taking up a stone, he squeezed it until a stream of water poured out of it.

Nothing daunted, the little tailor took from his pocket the cheese. This he squeezed until out poured a stream of whey.

"So!" growled the giant, thinking the cheese a stone, "match this, little tailor!"

With that, he picked up another stone and flung it as far as the eye could see. The little tailor, smiling to himself, then drew from his pocket the bird that sheltered there.

When he flung it into the air, it flew over the trees and beyond the far horizon.

"Never have I seen a stone thrown so far!" cried the giant.

Thinking he was no match for the little tailor, he took leave and went on his way.

The little tailor, too, marched on — always following his nose. At length, it led him to the king's palace.

Being very weary, he at once lay down in the courtyard and fell sound asleep. Many people looked at him curiously and read the words he had stitched on his belt.

"Seven at one blow!" they murmered, backing away from him. "The King must hear of this!"

Presently, a messenger came and asked the little tailor to enter the king's service.

"That is why I have come," he replied.

And so it was done.

The rest of the king's soldiers were most displeased. But they feared to bait the little tailor to a fight, lest he kill them all — seven at each blow of his sword!

Instead, they went to the king and asked to be discharged, at once, from his service.

Now the king trembled for himself.

So great a warrior as this little tailor might, in time, wrest away his throne!

To be rid of him, the king sent the little tailor to kill two giants who lived nearby.

"Rid my kingdom of these giants who rob and plunder by night," said the king, "and you shall wed my only daughter — and have half of my land as well."

"I'll do that," said the little tailor. "He who kills seven at one blow need not fear but two."

And off he marched, still following his nose, to the woods where the giants lived.

Finding them sleeping — and snoring so

that the trees themselves trembled — the little tailor filled his pockets with stones.

Nimbly, he climbed a tree and hid himself in the branches above the giants' heads. He then dropped one stone after another on the chest of the first of the giants.

"Ho!" cried the giant, waking and pushing the other. "Why are you hitting me?"

"I'm not!" growled the other, and soon both were asleep and snoring again.

Now the little tailor began dropping stones on the chest of the second giant.

"This is too much!" roared the giant.

And, thinking that the first giant had been hitting him, he pulled up a tree and went at him with all his might.

A terrible battle took place.

At its end, the woods were strewn with uprooted oaks, and both giants lay dead.

Down from the tree came the little tailor.

"The deed is done," he told the king. "I have killed both giants — and I claim your daughter's hand in marriage, and half of your lands and riches as well."

The brave little tailor was, therefore, dressed in princely garments and married — in all pomp and ceremony — to the princess.

When it came his turn to rule the kingdom, his enemies feared the man who had killed seven at one blow. But his subjects came to love him for his wisdom and for the gentleness that had once caused him to shelter a small, weary bird.

And so it was that the little tailor remained — for all his lifetime — a simple, wise, and happy king.

POST CARD

Dear Jack Rabbits all,
   Stopped just overnight in Belgium-to give your regards to the Belgian hares. Fine looking chaps, big and spotted— though rather tame.
   They send greetings, as does
Your friend, Koa Koala

To the Jack Rabbits
All over the Plains
Australia 07059

The Wonderful Fishing Rod

ONLY LAST YEAR, on pleasant evenings in the French town of Chaville, Nicolas and his grandpère had always gone fishing together.

It was Grandpère who would drop his line into the Seine. But it was Nicolas who watched for a fish to take the bait.

Then Grandpère would pull up his line.

On the hook there would be a fish — sometimes so small that it was thrown back.

Sometimes a fish large enough to cook.

And sometimes a fish so large that Grandpère would swell with pride.

"Look!" he would say, holding it up for all his cronies to see. "A fine one, eh? This shows that Grandpère Leroux is not yet in his dotage — is it not so?"

Then he and Nicolas would walk home tall and proud!

But one great fish put an end to all such happiness. It was so enormous that when Grandpère tried to pull it up, SNAP! his fishing rod broke in two.

What a calamity!

"It is fate," said Grandpère Leroux. "It shows that at best I am but a boastful old man — fit only to sit on a bench!"

And from that time on, instead of going fishing with Nicolas, Grandpère would sit alone in the dying light, hunched over the pieces on his chessboard.

This made Nicolas feel so sad!

"Perhaps," he thought as it neared Grandpère's birthday, "if I get him a new fishing rod, he will try his luck again."

Nicolas went at once to look at fishing rods. One was wonderful — slender but strong, and with a fine whip to it.

Cat

Swaggering
Squalling,
Scrounging
For fish heads
Under the bridge,
A cat —
And it meant
For a lap,
Warmth against
Deeper warmth,
To cradle
Its pebbled
Purring.

"Madame Mignonette," he said, "will you give me work at one franc a day?"

"It would be a pleasure," said Madame Mignonette. "That is, mon petit, if you can make change quickly."

Nicolas could not make change at all.

How could he, when he would not enter school until the fall?

So he went to the fish stalls.

Now, Madame Escargot needed help.

But she couldn't engage Nicolas, who

But the price!

It cost five francs more than Nicolas had saved in an entire year, and here was Grand-père's birthday not a week away.

For a moment, Nicolas was in despair.

Then, seeing that the market was very busy these days, he thought he might earn those five important francs.

He went first to the flower stall.

did not yet know how to read the numbers that told the weight of her fish.

Nicolas could not work for Monsieur Brie, either. He was much too small to lift the heavy wheels of cheese — let alone use the great, sharp knife to cut wedges.

"Come back when you are bigger than a mouthful," said Monsieur Brie. "I will then gladly engage you at your price."

Sadly, Nicolas turned away.

And sadly he started home.

On the street just before his own, men were busily digging up the pavement.

What a noise!

To make it worse, Monsieur Croissant, the baker, was shouting at them and waving his arms. He even tore at his own beard!

"Stop the noise!" he cried. "Clear up the debris — and put my street in good order again. As it is now, no customers will come for my warm crusty bread!"

But the workmen went on working.

And the baker went on shouting.

Then, suddenly, Nicolas had an idea.

"Monsieur Croissant," he said, "I will take the bread to your customers — if you will pay one franc a day for five days."

Monsieur Croissant was overjoyed.

"Gladly, petit!" he cried.

So Nicolas went running home to get his red car, the one that Grandpère had given him for his fifth birthday.

And, as well, to get his maman's permission to deliver the bread.

It was not only agreeable to Maman.

She asked Nicolas to bring her one loaf each day when he came home from work.

So Nicolas delivered Monsieur Croissant's long loaves of warm crusty bread every day for five days.

Monsieur Croissant was pleased, as were his customers. So, of course, was Nicolas's maman — who had one less errand to do.

Most pleased of all was Nicolas himself. For, at the end of each day, he had one more franc for the wonderful fishing rod.

At the end of five days, as luck would have it, Monsieur Croissant's street was all in good order again.

"For this good luck," he said happily, "you must have a bit of luck too, Nicolas."

And, will you believe it, he gave Nicolas an extra franc — to buy sweets!

But first, even before he went to the bonbonnerie, Nicolas bought the wonderful fishing rod for his grandpère's birthday.

The day was celebrated with a splendid dinner and much good company.

Already, a week has passed since then.

And again, near the bridge over the Seine, sit Nicolas and his Grandpère Leroux.

Together (of course with the help of the wonderful fishing rod) they have caught the largest fish in the entire river.

"Only look!" cries Grandpère, holding up that great fish. "Here it is my sixtieth year, and this is a fish to show that Grandpère Leroux still has strength and vigor!"

"Unquestionably!" call his cronies, very pleased to have him back. "There is no doubt but you will outlive us all!"

Nicolas is proud of the gift he has given his grandpère. But modestly, he bows his head to again put bait on the hook of the wonderful fishing rod.

Poor Little Jeanne Marie

In Brittany, they said to me,
"Come see our morning's catch
Of fish — to sell at les Halles,
Or we'd cook you a batch!"

In Normandy, they said to me,
"Come see our lettuce, petite,
And all our tender vegetables —
To market, mind, not eat!"

In Burgundy, they said to me,
"Come see our grapes — too fine
To eat — for they are sure to make
A most superior wine!"

At home at last, they said of me,
"She's fallen asleep — how nice!"
And dined (while I was asleep)
On luscious bouillabaisse —

All full of fish from Brittany,
With salad — fresh from Normandy,
And sparkling wine from Burgundy,
And — not a taste — for me!

The Adventures of Pantaloon

PANTALOON, exuberant poodle that he is, is loose in the Luxembourg Gardens.

Having played havoc with a flower border, he digs a trench in the lawn in an effort to dislodge a burrowing mole.

Then, bursting out of nearby bushes, he puts a rather cross old lady to flight.

And from there, Pantaloon splashes into the lake to play tag with the swans.

The cygnets are terrified!

Their swan parents — hissing furiously — take after the dripping poodle.

Off he races, in such a hurry to avoid them that he overturns the puppet show.

Then, meeting head on with the balloon man, Pantaloon cannot resist the temptation to borrow his great bouquet of bright bobbing balloons.

On he goes — now with two swans, the puppeteer, his audience of seven small children, and the balloon man after him.

No one can catch that wicked Pantaloon!

Not even the gendarme, who has been summoned by the now *very* cross old lady.

"Stop thief!" the gendarme cries, blowing his whistle as he runs.

"Never!" barks Pantaloon.

Swift as lightning, he races to the pony rides — and round and round the track he goes. The ponies and donkeys think it is a race to the finish! Away they all go, pushing and shoving, neighing and braying, as each tries to outrun that wicked Pantaloon. The pony master is indignant!

As a last resort, the gendarme telephones the dogcatcher to come and help.

Now the children are alarmed.

"Stop, Pantaloon!" they call. "Be reasonable, or you will wind up in the pound!"

But Pantaloon has gone berserk.

With the balloons bobbing above his head, he races out of the park and into the traffic on the Boulevard St. Michel.

Brakes screech as motorists try to avoid hitting the reckless poodle — and his long line of pursuers.

There is, nevertheless, a three-car collision. Although no one is injured, the motorists blame one another.

Fists begin to fly.

The entire quarter is in an uproar!

Then suddenly, as if from nowhere, a fat sausage — on the end of a long, stout cord — is dangled before Pantaloon's nose.

The runaway lets go the balloons (which are quickly retrieved by the balloon man) and snaps at the tempting morsel.

Once, twice, three times he snaps.

But each time Pantaloon misses.

It is tantalizing!

That sausage — always just out of his reach — leads Pantaloon swiftly back into the Luxembourg Gardens. It takes him directly to a bench under a chestnut tree where sits his master, Monsieur Bobo, in deep conversation with a young lady who is also of the circus.

As the sausage is then drawn up — into the very heavens, it seems — Pantaloon leaps up and down, barking so loudly that at last Monsieur Bobo is aware of him.

"Is it you, Pantaloon?" he cries.

Crawling under the bench, Monsieur Bobo finds that the harness at the end of Pantaloon's leash is indeed empty.

"It *is* you, Pantaloon!" he cries.

And, since Pantaloon's pursuers are rapidly approaching, he takes a quick leave of

the young lady. Keeping to the bushes, Monsieur Bobo and Pantaloon are soon out of the park, heading safely for their pension on the Left Bank.

When the two swans, the puppeteer, the seven small children, the balloon man, the gendarme, *and* the dogcatcher arrive at the bench under the chestnut tree — no one is there except a young lady rouging her lips.

"A strange business, this!" says the gendarme to the dogcatcher.

"A splendid business," the seven small children whisper among themselves. "Our beloved Pantaloon has been saved!"

Then, high above the thrust of the Eiffel Tower, they see a most marvelous gas balloon sweeping southward toward Spain.

In its basket sits someone small, and grey, and altogether amiable-looking.

"Something *had* to be done," this small

traveler observes to himself. "It is fortunate that I happened to have a long, stout cord tucked away in my pocket."

And, munching thoughtfully on the fat sausage, Koa Koala — in his marvelous gas balloon — is wafted off into the fast-gathering mists of evening.

My Great Aunt Lives in Tours

SMALL GIRLS AND BOYS in France enjoy playing this add-to-the-jingle game.

Sitting in a circle, they all say:

My great aunt lives in Tours
In a house with a cherry tree,
With a little mouse, squeak,
squeak!
And a big black dog, woof, woof!

Each child, in turn, repeats the verse and adds the name and sound of another object (animal, clock, bell, etc.).

The game ends when a player forgets a line, or when everyone is laughing too hard to go any farther with the jingle!

Luis Ortega's Wagon

Luis Ortega is making a wagon.

"When it is made," he tells his small sister, "one day, I will put you in it. I will pull you all through our city of Barcelona — to the park."

His small sister laughs and claps her hands.

Day after day, she watches Luis work.

At last the wagon is finished.

On a Saturday, when there is no school, Luis Ortega does put his small sister in the new wagon. And away they go.

It is a long, long walk.

But on and on goes Luis Ortega, pulling the wagon through the narrow russet-colored streets.

Suddenly, one wheel breaks away from the wagon. Out tumbles Luis Ortega's small sister, all in a squalling heap!

It is the end of Luis's plan.

And it is suppertime before he — carrying his small sister and pulling the three-wheeled wagon — is back home again. His mother is crying. The neighbors are very angry.

"How your poor mother works to keep you!" they cry. "Poor widow that she is, and you to worry her so!"

Luis Ortega hangs his head.

"I meant only to give the small sister a happy day," he says. "To have her play in the beautiful playground — like the children in the great house where my mother works all day."

"Ah," says their neighbor Señora Alvarez. "The beautiful playground of Gaudi."

"A beautiful place to go!" says her husband, looking less angry than before.

He looks at Luis Ortega's broken wagon.

"A fine wagon," he says. "But not for a trip like that — all across Barcelona!"

"No?" asks Luis Ortega sadly. "We can never go then, even when it is fixed?"

"No-o-o-o!" says Señor Alvarez, making the word sound long and sad. "Not in this wagon."

"But in your wagon, Alvarez!" cries his wife. "In your wagon, with your horse, it would be possible to go — yes?"

"No!" says Señor Alvarez crossly.

Then, scowling at his wife, he says, "Allow me to think for myself, woman! Come, we go home now, to eat."

Off they go. And soon Luis Ortega and his mother and small sister have had their supper of bread with olive oil, and have gone quietly to bed.

In the morning, all three are up early to go to the great cathedral. It is beautiful there, so beautiful that Luis Ortega begins to think again of the beautiful playground that he and his small sister will never see.

But hola! When they are back at their own little house — there is Señor Alvarez's wagon out in front. His horse is decked with red and orange plumes, as if for a great fiesta.

In the wagon sits Señor Alvarez himself, and Señora Alvarez — holding an enormous basket heaped high with a picnic lunch! "Climb up, get in!" calls Señor Alvarez. "We all go to the Gaudi playground today!"

Into the big wagon hops Luis Ortega — and his small sister, and his mother — still dressed in their best.

All through Barcelona they ride, with Señor Alvarez's horse prancing — and its plumes tossing — until they come to the wonderful park.

"There!" shouts Señor Alvarez. "There is your playground by the great Gaudi. Go, Luis Ortega! Take your small sister, and play until your hearts sing!"

Luis Ortega wastes no time.

"See, here it is," he tells his sister. "The place I said I'd take you as soon as my wagon was finished —"

Now when Luis Ortega says "wagon," his heart — and his shoulders — begin to fall.

He has failed, hasn't he?

Failed in what he had planned to do.

But behind him booms the great voice of Señor Alvarez. "It is no shame to fail, Luis Ortega," he says. "By this you learn that no boy can do a man's job, until he himself is a man!"

And so Luis Ortega, smiling again and holding his small sister's hand, climbs up the hill to do a boy's job — of playing, and hiding, and seeking, and sliding — all the rest of that fine and festive spring day.

The Small Contessa

Lɪsᴀ lives in Rome.

Her full name — Contessa Elisabeta Maria Ilena Constancia Margarita Milano di Silva — is a very grand one.

Lisa's home is big and grand as well.

It is filled with servants, and stairways hung with paintings, and gleaming musical instruments — all of which Lisa must learn to play — and with elegant guests forever coming to visit her father.

"A splendid way of life, Lisa!" says Fräulein, the small contessa's governess.

But Lisa does not think it splendid.

She does not like her many lessons.

Nor learning to curtsy, and to dance.

She does not like the sedate walks she must take with Fräulein every afternoon. Not even when they go to the square to feed the pigeons that bow, and bob, and walk on pink feet across the ancient tiles.

All that Lisa does like is her riding class. And all that she loves is the summertime, when her family moves to their villa in the hills where the olives grow.

There Lisa can ride every day.

There she may dress as she pleases.

And there she can lie on a hill — lazy as the breeze — watching the white clouds form and change in the blue Italian sky.

"They look like sheep," says Giulio, the shepherd boy for that particular hill.

"Like the dome of St. Peter's," says Fräulein, crossing herself.

"Like the milk-white Lippizan horses," says Lisa's father who has just ridden up.

"What horses are they?" asks Lisa.

"Those at the Spanish Riding School in Vienna," her father says. "One thinks he can ride until he has seen them. After, he knows what riding — and discipline — are."

At once, Lisa jumps up. With bright eyes, she begs to be taken to see those horses.

Her father studies her from head to toe.

"Sometime, perhaps," he says. "When you are ready for Vienna. There — attend please — one may not dress haphazardly. Good manners are required always —

"Also," he adds, "one must have learning to enjoy beauty. Yes, Lisa, when you are ready we will go to see the Lippizans."

Lisa stands thoughtfully on one leg.

Then she mounts her horse and rides thoughtfully back to the villa.

All summer in the hills, and all fall and winter in Rome, she thinks of the promise her father has made.

She works very hard to please Fräulein, even her schoolroom papers are careful.

One day in spring, Fräulein presents herself to Lisa's father.

"You will not believe the change, Excellency," she says. "The small Lisa also curtsies charmingly — and dances like a flower blowing in the wind!"

"Good," says Lisa's father. "And when you walk in the afternoons?"

"All eyes are on her!" says Fräulein.

"Send Lisa to me," her father says, and when she comes, he takes her hand.

"It is time, Lisa," he says, "for our visit to Vienna to see the Lippizan horses."

"I thank you, Father," Lisa says gravely. Gravely, she curtsies.

Gravely and gracefully, she walks from the room and into the great hall. But once there, Lisa races — wild as a wild colt — up the great stairs to tell Fräulein.

What a racket she makes!

But what would you expect? Not even a contessa can be grave and sedate at all times.

And Elisabeta Maria Ilena Constancia Margarita Milano di Silva is still a very small contessa, after all!

Fisherman's Son

Athens, they say,
Would take your breath away
With mighty ruins,
Golden on her climbing sunlit hills by day,
And white and ancient as the stars
By still and awesome night.

But Mykonos,
My island, is a place to breathe
More free in sunlight,
To know the ways of octopus and pelican,
And when the Voreas blows, to sleep
To song of windmill sails.

Into the Alps

IN MANY SWISS VILLAGES, on one particular day in spring, the cows are driven up into the Alps.

What a commotion on that day!

Dogs bark. Mules grumble as they are loaded with food and bedding. People hurry about, carrying cheeses, potatoes, and pickles.

The cows — tired of being cooped up all through the winter — moo angrily.

But now the herdsmen go to bell them, to deck them with spring flowers, and to lead them out in the fresh, spring air.

When all is ready, the head herdsman gives a signal. The procession of cows and loaded mules and men, women, and children goes through the village and into the mountains.

Blue Slope

The edelweiss,
Its flowers as white as snow,
Has gone — gone with the snow
To higher, colder slopes.
Instead, these hills
Are blue with gentians.
Come, pick them now with me
For crowns, and necklaces,
And clustered handfuls, to bring
The deep blue Alpine sky
Indoors — for just one day
And starry night.

Up and up and up they all climb, to the jangling of cowbells, the shouts of the men, and the chatter and laughter of the women and the little girls and boys.

It is noon when they come to the first of the green mountain pastures — bright with the bloom of the alpine wildflowers.

The cows eat hungrily. Grass and gentian flowers are all one to them!

Men and boys unpack the mules, while the women open and air out the small chalets where their families will stay.

Then a fire is built, and soon the families are eating raclette — the hot, melted cheese dish of this day — with boiled potatoes, and the tangiest of pickles.

Later the animals must be given water, and the heavy-uddered cows must be milked. In days to come, there will be the hard work of mountain herding, and making cheese, and sending milk to the village every day.

But what is work on this first day in the mountain air! There is singing, and yodelling, and dancing as well, is there not?

By evening, the little girls and boys are ready to tumble into fresh-made beds. They drift into sleep looking at the jars of wildflowers they have gathered, and listening to the slow jangle of cowbells.

Last of all, they may perhaps think of the many happy days they will have in the Alps, before the men and cows go up to still higher mountain pastures, and they — and their mothers — go back to their everyday life in the village below.

POST CARD

HELVETIA 10

Dear Mr. Addison, and all,

We are over the Matterhorn.
   What a sight!
And what a sound! Oh help!
Balloon has nicked
   himself on a rocky
crag-gas is seeping out
with an ominous hiss.

More later,
   I hope! Koa Koala

To Mr. Addison,
   Balloon Man
Somewhere in Sydney Zoo
Sydney, Australia 11127

Two Boys of Austria

Long ago, in Rohau in Lower Austria, there lived a boy who thought only of music.

His father was a wheelwright, and his mother a pastry cook. Poor as they were, their house was filled with the sound of the father's harp — and the songs of the family.

The small boy, Josef, came to sing so sweetly that — when he was only eight — he was asked to join the choir at St. Stephen's church in beautiful Vienna.

For many years, he studied and worked hard at his music. At times he went hungry. And at times, he was little more than a servant who played music for a wealthy man — or a music-loving prince.

But Josef had a happy nature. Everywhere he could learn. And always he listened to — and wrote down — the music that was inside him.

He played concerts in many cities, and little by little, people came to love the delicate, enchanting music of Josef Haydn.

Josef himself never believed that his music was everything he wanted it to be. Even when he had become world-famous, he thought far more of the music of another man than of his own.

The music that Josef Haydn so loved was that of a young man — Wolfgang Mozart.

As a boy, Wolfgang, too, had been close to music. But whether for love of it, or because of his father, would be hard to say.

When he was six, he wrote music and played it so well that his father took him from town to town to play for great crowds.

This earned food at least for the two.

But nowhere could Wolfgang find a patron to support him in exchange for enjoying the music he wrote and played.

At last, he did find such a patron. But when the boy's music grew famous, his patron grew jealous. He kept the young Mozart in such poverty and slavery that the boy had to leave.

He went, quite penniless, to Vienna. As he struggled for a living, the music Mozart played became even more beautiful. His fame, like that of Josef Haydn, spread all over Europe.

In time, the music of Mozart came to be considered even greater than that of the master Papa Haydn. Perhaps Wolfgang Mozart had within him a genius that drove him harder.

The Milk-White Horses

THE HOFBURG, IN VIENNA, is a huge sprawling palace of great age. One of the clustered buildings is that of the Spanish Riding School.

Within, it looks like the largest and most beautiful of opera houses.

But really, it is an arena.

The vast floor, spread with tanbark, is ready for the entrance of the Lippizan horses. The waiting crowd gasps as, at last, they come trotting in.

Milk-white, snow-white, cloud-white, the Lippizan horses toss their proud heads and eye their smartly-dressed trainers.

They parade around the arena in changing forms — two abreast, four abreast, six abreast, and in single file.

They jump and turn as if on wings.

Then, to bright Viennese music, the Lippizan horses waltz — like guests at a royal ball — around the vast arena.

Suddenly, as suddenly as it began, the magnificent performance comes to an end.

"Bravo! Bravo!" shouts the crowd.

The Lippizan horses and their trainers bow and bow again. When the last milk-white, snow-white, cloud-white horse has gone, the crowd rouses itself to leave.

Out of the hall they stroll, people from all parts of Europe, and of the world.

And among them, sedate at her father's side — but with shining eyes — strolls Elisabeta Maria Ilena Constancia Margarita Milano di Silva.

The small contessa has seen the magnificent Lippizan horses at last.

Have Courage, Koa Koala!

Hiss-s-s! Hiss-s-s!

The gas was still seeping out of Koa Koala's marvelous gas balloon — and the balloon itself was rapidly losing altitude.

"I wonder," said Koa, looking down on a great number of noble peaks, "on exactly which peak we will descend?"

Fortunately, the balloon came smoothly down on a high green hill, and Koa Koala hopped out to inspect the damage.

The nick in his balloon was not large.

Still, Koa had neither gas nor a sticking plaster for patching the hole.

So he called "Hello!" with all his might.

Then he called, "Help!"

For all the answer he got, Koa might as well have been on the very top of nowhere!

It was most discouraging.

But as Koa Koala stood there wondering what in the world to do, a nun came striding over the rise.

Serenely smiling, she came toward Koa and his shrinking balloon. And behind her, all with knapsacks, came a troup of small, rosy-cheeked girls and boys.

In a moment they had gathered around Koa and his once marvelous — and now rather limp — gas balloon.

"There's a leak wants fixing," Koa explained. "And we need some gas. Naturally, the lighter-than-air kind."

The girls and boys stood round-eyed.

Not a word had they understood.

They turned to the nun, who talked to them in a language quite foreign to Koa. Then she, and the girls and boys, went hurrying off in all directions.

"To get help, I hope!" thought Koa.

But presently, back came the girls with armfuls of wildflowers for Koa.

Then back came the boys, with a pail of fresh goat's milk for him to try.

"Delicious!" said Koa, sipping some.

The children, delighted to see him in good cheer, quickly opened their knapsacks and spread out a splendid picnic lunch.

Koa sat down and ate hungrily, all the while keeping a wary eye on his balloon.

To keep his mind off that, the girls and boys began singing the loudest and merriest of Tyrolean songs.

All this was charming indeed.

But suddenly, with a last despairing hiss, the marvelous gas balloon collapsed in a despairing and crumpled heap!

"It is the end!" cried Koa Koala.

But no, it was not the end.

From beyond the rise, there came a chugging and clanking sound — and then an ancient truck came rolling along.

The nun, still smiling serenely, rode on one running board. On the other — Koa could not believe it — stood a balloon man, with balloons bobbing over his head.

Down he jumped.

From the truck, he took a large tankful of exactly the right kind of gas.

"The lighter-than-air kind!" cried Koa.

The marvelous gas balloon was soon pumped full — yet not too full. Once it was taut, the nun covered the nick in its side with a sturdy square of mustard plaster.

"A splendid operation!" cried Koa Koala. "And a splendid recovery!"

The marvelous gas balloon, as good as new, was bobbing and ready to go. With his paws full of wildflowers, and his face wreathed in smiles, Koa hopped aboard.

Then up, up, up went the marvelous gas balloon — higher than the highest snow-capped peak in all the Tyrolean Alps.

The nun waved and smiled serenely.

The little girls threw kisses.

The boys waved their hats.

The balloon man waved his balloons.

"Thank you!" called Koa Koala.

"*Merci! Grazie!*" he called, racking his brains for just the right word.

Then, "*Danke shön!*" he called jubilantly to all his beaming friends far, far below.

And Koa Koala and his marvelous gas balloon were once more safely on their way around the whole wide world.

The Bright Eggs of Easter

IN SPRING, AND EVEN BEFORE, women all over Czechoslovakia are busy making the most intricate of Easter eggs.

First, to be sure, the whites and yolks of the eggs must be blown out. This is done through pinholes — one at the top and one at the bottom of each egg.

A breathless job it is, too.

Then each egg must be coated with wax.

Delicate, intricate designs are scratched into the waxen surface. Each egg is then dipped into brightly-colored dye.

More designs are scratched on the waxed egg, and this time another color is used.

Again, again, and again, new designs are scratched on the egg before it is dipped into another brightly-colored dye.

At last — all over Czechoslovakia — the fragile eggs are finished.

Some are threaded with loops to hang on Egg Trees — bare branches firmly set in decorated clay pots.

Some are nested in baskets to grace the Easter tables of families who live all over Czechoslovakia.

And some — the most beautiful eggs of all — are given as gifts on Easter Day.

"Joy!" say the givers, as they pass their finest eggs on to others.

"Joy!" say those who receive them into careful hands.

For the Easter egg, in Czechoslovakia as in many, many other countries, stands for the new life that comes in spring.

The new budding of trees.

The new blossoming of flowers.

The coming of new animals into the world — the lamb, the calf, the duckling, and the stumbling, chirping chick.

And, in no way least, the new happiness that comes to people everywhere when their world turns from winter into spring.

The Incomparable Egg

In Moscow, late on the night before Easter, Natasha Ivanova was still awake and wondering about the incomparable egg.

She knew that her Great-Aunt Sofia had come to visit, for had she not heard the car come driving up?

Had she not heard the front door flung open, and her father and mother welcoming her Great-Aunt Sofia?

That she had.

Natasha Ivanova had also heard the mysterious rustling of packages — fresh baked bread from the country house, perhaps!

But had Great-Aunt Sofia brought the incomparable egg with her this time?

If she had, it would be on the table at this very moment — with the cold moonlight glowing on its pale blue sides, and glinting on its delicate gold filigree.

Thinking of that, Natasha Ivanova slipped out of her bed and into her slippers.

She tiptoed out of her room.

And down the hall.

And into the big room.

Then — hardly daring to — she looked on the table near the window.

And there it was, the incomparable egg!

Just as she had imagined, the egg was glowing pale, pale blue in the moonlight. The gold filigree and the little gold catch on the door were gleaming, too.

That egg was so beautiful that when Natasha picked it up, she could not make herself put it down.

Instead, holding it in both hands, she carried it back to her own tiny room. She set it on her table in the moonlight.

And there it glowed and gleamed all through the night — with Natasha Ivanova smiling in her sleep beside it.

But in the morning, there was a great commotion in the apartment.

"The egg — the Fabergé egg!" cried Natasha's mother. "It is gone!"

"Gone?" asked Irina Alexandrova (who shared the apartment). "How can it be gone?"

"Stolen, beyond a doubt," replied her husband. "It is of great value, that egg."

"Aha, you know that!" Natasha's father cried. "Perhaps you have made off with it!"

"Well then," said Natasha Ivanova's big brother, "we must call the police!"

"Scoundrels, to think such a thing!" shouted Irina and Alexi Alexandrov.

In a moment, everyone was shouting, or sobbing, or crying, "It's jail for the thief — of that you may be sure!"

"Jail!" thought Natasha Ivanova. "It is I who will be put in jail!"

All the same, she slipped out of her warm bed and into her cold slippers.

She picked up the egg — the incomparable egg — and crept out of the room.

Down the hall she tiptoed, and into the big room full of big, angry people.

There Natasha Ivanova held up the Fabergé egg for all to see.

"I — I took it," she said. "But just to look at it in the moonlight."

Then, putting the incomparable egg on the table, Natasha Ivanova said, "Now I must dress before the police come for me."

"The police?" said her father. "There will be no police in here!"

"Never!" said her mother, wrapping her own warm shawl around her little girl.

"Unless," said Alexi Alexandrov, "I call them to report your false charges!"

"A thousand pardons, Alexi!" said Natasha's father, his face growing red.

"It is over then, friend," Alexi replied.

It was then that Great-Aunt Sofia came sweeping into the room.

"What is this?" she asked. "In Moscow, is it the custom to shout like the roosters at the very moment of dawn?"

All at the same time, the Alexandrovs and the Ivanovs told Great-Aunt Sofia what had happened.

"So that was it!" she cried.

And throwing back her head and laughing, she took Natasha Ivanova on her lap.

"Natasha," she said, "now I will tell you a story about the incomparable egg."

Great-Aunt Sofia said that it had once belonged to her own Great-Aunt Katerina. And that she herself — as a small girl — had loved it as Natasha Ivanova did now.

"One night — the night before Easter —

I, too, took the Fabergé egg to my room."

"To watch it glow and gleam in the moonlight?" asked Natasha Ivanova.

"Precisely," said Great-Aunt Sofia. "And as a consequence, my Great-Aunt Katerina left the egg to me when she died."

"Ah-h-h!" sighed Irina Alexandrova. "To you who admired the Fabergé egg so very much!"

"It is so," said Great-Aunt Sofia. "But I will not wait so many years —"

Reaching out, she took up the incomparable egg and put it in the small hands of her Great-Niece Natasha Ivanova.

"It is yours, Natasha Ivanova," she said, smiling, "on this very Easter day."

And Natasha Ivanova — hardly daring to breathe — opened the catch of the pale, pale blue egg to admire the golden eagle so delicately fashioned by Fabergé in the far-off days of the rich and arrogant czars.

POST CARD

Dear Kiwi, and all,

All is well again! Balloon and I are safe, alive, and- at the moment- floating over the Black Sea. Which isn't black at all. It's getting warm, whew!

Your friend ever,

Koa Koala

To Kiwi at the Zoo
The Sydney Zoo
Sydney, Australia
11127

At Day's First Light

At day's first light,
The muezzim in our minaret
Calls everyone to prayer:
Allah-U-Ekber, he calls,
Allah-U-Ekber, Allah-U-Ekber,
At once from farther off
And farther, farther still,
The other muezzims
Call and call until
From every high, white minaret
The soaring words
Echo through all of Ankara:
Allah-U-Ekber, Allah-U-Ekber,
Allah-U-Ekber, Allah-U-Ekber!
And when the last voice
Fades, and all is still,
The sun glides up to paint
The many minarets in colors
As rich as any in the woven rug
I kneel on when I pray.

A Day To Remember

EACH MORNING, as soon as the sun was well up in their small village in Turkey, Abdul's mother would remind him of his chores.

She would tell him to feed his dog, and the chickens, to fill the jugs with water, to wash carefully, and to brush his shoes.

"And above all," she would say, "remember to put on your smock before you go to school."

"I will, my mother," Abdul said each day.

And when she had gone to work in the fields, he did do all of his chores. Often, he wished that his mother would not remind him — over and over and over again — all through the year.

At last, looking like his father when he was cross, Abdul asked her to stop.

"I know my chores," he said.

The next day, his mother said not a word about dog, or chickens, or water, or washing, or shoes, or smock.

"What happiness!" thought Abdul.

So free and proud did he feel that he went racing — barefoot at that — out into the sunlight. Around and around the small house he ran, arms waving and feet stamping.

He saw his friend Kemal, and together they wrestled for a bit in the dusty street.

Then Abdul called to the calling birds.

And he set his dog chasing after the cat of their neighbor, Ali Bey.

Such excitement there was then!

"Catch your dog, Abdul!" shouted Ali Bey, shaking his fist. "Then be off to school, or you'll be late — and the teacher will have something to say about that!"

Now Abdul's dog was no easy dog to catch. When he had done that, there was barely time for Abdul to slip into his shoes before hurrying off to school.

His teacher was not pleased with him.

"No smock, Abdul?" she asked.

Before Abdul could answer, she noticed the dust on his face and clothes.

"Go outside and wash," she said, looking like a storm cloud. "And have the kindness to brush off the dust as well."

The other children — even including Kemal — laughed at Abdul.

It was, in all, not a good day at school.

And when Abdul was back home at last, things were even worse.

The hungry chickens were squawking as if they were, one and all, being boiled for supper — and that alive!

The rooster, having torn Abdul's mother's pepper plant to bits, was up on the roof crowing as if to greet the sunrise.

And Abdul's dog, too famished to wait for Abdul to feed her, was chasing Ali Bey's sheep — as if she would devour them all.

Abdul clapped his forehead.

He hardly knew where to start!

But first he caught Dervish, that wicked beggar of a dog, and shut her in the house.

Next he fed the hens and the rooster.

Then he tied up what was left of his mother's bedraggled pepper plant.

And then — before she and his father

should come home from the fields — Abdul filled seven jugs with water.

To be on the safe side, he filled all of Ali Bey's jugs as well.

"It's to say that I'm sorry my dog chased your cat and sheep, Ali Bey," he said.

Now Ali Bey clapped *his* forehead.

"My sheep, too?" he cried angrily.

Then, seeing his filled water jugs, Ali Bey looked somewhat less angry.

"Well, it is no great matter," he said. "Fill the sheep's watering trough, Abdul,

Abdul's day had not been a good one.

At once, she began to make köfte—Abdul's father's favorite dish—though it was not yet time for a meal with meat.

So when Abdul's father came home there was much good cheer in the small house.

Later, Abdul cleaned his father's shoes as well as his own. He laid out his school smock, too. Then, quiet as he had never been, Abdul went to bed.

In the morning, surprisingly enough, Abdul's mother did not remind him to do all his chores before he went to school.

Nor did she remind him ever again.

But then, after that day—a day to remember it had been—Abdul never again forgot to feed the dog and the chickens, to bring water and to wash himself, or to clean his shoes and put on his smock before he set out for school.

nd we will say no more about it."

Abdul did that gladly.

He lit the fire for supper, too.

Still, when his mother came home, she eemed to know—as mothers do—that

Coffee Cups

N THE TURKISH GAME of Coffee Cups, here are two teams each having five or ix players.

Each team has four cups, set upside down n front of it, and a single token.

One team must go out of the room while he other hides its token under one of its our coffee cups.

When the first team comes back, one of ts players must try his best to guess which cup covers the token.

If he does, his team wins one point and has a turn at hiding its token secretly.

Now the other team does the guessing, and so the game goes on. At its end, the eam with the greatest number of points is declared Coffee Cup Champion.

Work Song

This is the land
Of our fathers, their land
Of milk and honey.
For us, it is a harsh land,
A new land, a land to fashion
With our own bare hands
In labor dawn-to-dark.
The labor is joy!
Once again, milk is flowing
From pastures that lay barren,
And honey from blossoms
Of our planting.
In times of our children,
The green bay tree
Will scent the air,
And voices of the turtle dove
Be heard again in the land
Of our fathers.

Nomi and the Sabra

WHEN DAVID FIRST CAME to live on the kibbutz, Nomi was very proud of him.

"He's cute, and smart, too," her friend Ruth said. "I like David."

"And he's going to play the violin for our teacher's wedding," said Hagar. "Did you know that?"

"Of course I knew," Nomi said. "David is my own cousin, isn't he?"

She sounded, and looked, so proud that her friends didn't like it one bit.

They were glad when they could tell Nomi something not so good about David.

"He cries every single night after his father and mother go back to their own quarters," said Ruth.

"After two whole weeks here," said Hagar. "David's just a crybaby!"

"He is not!" Nomi said.

"Is too," said Ruth. "My brother is in the same room — so he ought to know."

Nomi had no answer to that.

So she just went to look for David.

He was busy taking care of the school pets — and cleaning their cages.

With her hands on her hips, and a scowl on her face, she said, "I hear you're a cry-baby, David — and you can just stop!"

"I wish I could," said David, closing the door of the rabbits' cage.

"Nomi," he said, "I like being here all day. But at night, after my mom and dad go, it's so different and strange."

David shrugged. "At home," he said, "we all lived in the same house. And at night, I could always hear my parents talking and laughing and all — and now —"

"And now," said Nomi, "this is your home, and you can just stop crying or I'll tell your dad about it!"

David didn't want that.

More than anything, he wanted to be a good Israeli like his father.

So after that, Nomi's cousin David didn't cry in the night anymore.

But something else happened.

David didn't laugh in the daytime.

He didn't eat much at mealtimes.

And he was very quiet all the time.

Their teacher, Miss Anna Sholem, noticed. She asked Nomi what was troubling David.

But Nomi wouldn't tell.

"Nothing's wrong," she said. "David likes living in our own country, where all of us must help — and be strong and brave."

"All right, Nomi," said Miss Sholem.

But she gave Nomi a sharp look. It made Nomi feel uncomfortable inside herself. So she went to watch her father, who was

working in the newly planted fruit groves.

He checked the apricot trees, and the pomegranates, and he clucked his tongue.

"We need more water here," he told the other men. "The transplants aren't doing as well as they should."

Nomi watched the men working on that.

When they took a break, she asked her father what transplants meant.

"Plants brought here from other places, Nomi," he said. "They need extra care to get used to new soil, and a new climate."

"Oh," said Nomi.

But she still looked puzzled, so her father pointed out beyond the kibbutz to the dry land, where nothing grew except the spiny cactus called sabra.

"The sabra grows without care," he said, "because it always grew here in the Negev. It's native to Israel — that's why people who were born here are called Sabra, too."

At last Nomi understood.

She nodded her head.

And she went looking for David again.

He was standing all alone, and very quiet, in the playground.

"David," Nomi said very softly, "David, you can cry at night if you want to — I won't tell anybody. I promise."

"Will you say I'm a crybaby?" David asked.

And Nomi said, "No, I won't."

Then she told David about the transplants, and about the sabra.

"You're a transplant, David," she said. "So I guess you just need more water than the Sabra like me."

David wasn't sure what Nomi was talking about. But he knew she was smiling.

So, at last, he smiled, too.

And that night, when David knew he dared cry if he wanted to — he found out that he didn't feel like crying anymore.

The next day, he was hungry again.

He ate like a horse!

He felt like laughing, too.

And he stopped being so quiet.

When it was time for Miss Anna Sholem's wedding, David was himself again.

He played the violin for the dancing, and the music was so merry that everyone clapped and sang between dances.

"I think David's great!" Hagar whispered to Nomi, and Nomi nodded.

"My brother says David's a good Israeli," whispered Ruth. "And since they sleep in the same room, my brother ought to know."

Nomi nodded again.

This time she smiled, too, and held out both her hands to Hagar and Ruth.

"Let's dance!" she said. "Let's all three of us dance this time together."

And away whirled the three small Sabra, Ruth, and Hagar, and Nomi. They twirled and stomped to the merry tune of the wed-

ding dance — which was played by the three grown-up musicians, and by David — that one, new and smiling small Israeli.

POST CARD

Dear Wallaby, etc.,

The Suez Canal looks like a great shortcut for everybody who lives around here. Too bad the countries keep fighting about who owns it.

Think I hear shooting right now—so away we go!

Yours (in a hurry),

Koa Koala

To Kangaroo, and etc.
At the Sydney Zoo
Sydney, Australia
11127

The Arab and the Camel

AN ARAB WAS RIDING HIS CAMEL across the desert when a great shamel began to blow.

Sand swept across the desert as in a blizzard. It stung the Arab's body even through his long thobe. And, in spite of his ghutra being drawn across his face, sand got into his nose and mouth.

The shamel even hid the sun so that all was darker, by far, than the night.

The Arab was forced to dismount.

With much difficulty — and no help at all from his camel, who whined and complained — he managed to put up his tent.

"I shall rest," he thought, crawling inside, "until the shamel ends."

But no sooner was the Arab inside, than his camel set up a great wailing.

"O master," it whined, "with no ghutra to shield my nose and mouth, the sand is choking me. Pray let me put only my muzzle in the tent that I may live to serve you!"

"Very well," said the Arab, taking pity on the creature and drawing up his legs to make room in the small tent.

In poked the camel's muzzle.

He blew sand all over the Arab.

And not content with that, he pleaded to put his long neck in the tent as well.

"Very well," said the Arab, remembering the stinging of sand on his own neck.

So presently the camel's long neck was thrust into the crowded tent.

"O my poor back and hump!" the camel wailed at once. "Having no thobe to cover them, they are being lashed as if with many cruel whips!"

Again the Arab let his heart be touched.

"Ease in your back and hump, Camel," he said, "only, take up as little space as you can."

This the camel did not do.

Instead, he pushed so strongly that the Arab was thrust out of the tent altogether.

The camel then drew his legs into the Arab's tent, spread himself out in great comfort, and went soundly asleep.

Not an inch of space was left for the poor Arab.

And plead as he did, his camel would not make room for him in his own tent!

The shamel lashed the poor man.

Sand filled his nose and mouth, and had not the grace of Allah ended the sandstorm, that would — in truth — have been the end of the Arab.

Giving thanks, the Arab took down his tent, packed it on the camel's back, and prodded the ungrateful creature awake.

"O master," cried the camel. "Do not mount me just yet — let me sleep a little to gain strength enough to carry you on your journey!"

This time the Arab was not touched.

"You have fooled me once," he said. "If I listen now, you will no doubt climb upon my back to ride, while I — your master — struggle and stumble to the next oasis!"

So saying, he flicked his whip, forcing the camel to rise to its great, spongy feet.

He mounted its back, as a master should.

And swearing to Allah never to listen to the miserable creature's pleas again, the Arab — much wiser than before — resumed his long journey across the desert.

Father of Misr

From Abyssinia
(So the storyteller sings),
The River Nile flows
Through Misr, branching
Like the fronds
Of the date palm,
Into the warm blue sea.

Where it flows,
The yellow-brown land
Of Misr flourishes green
With wheat and maize,
Earthnuts, sesame,
Marrow and cotton,
And blue-blossoming flax.

Then do the birds
Of Misr — the ibis, crow,
Hoopoe, and all others —
Rejoice at the greening
Along the river,
And thrum of frogs
Is heard on every breeze.

The oxen of Misr
Strain under their yokes,
The fellahin bend also
To their ancient plows;
Turning, the sakia
Spreads the water
Even to the farthest fields.

On flows the river,
Father of Misr, carrying
Boats laden with crops
To many towering cities
Where men gather
To buy and sell
The gifts of the Nile.

Past Giza, where stand
The great, ancient pyramids
And secret-smiling Sphinx,
The river flows onward,
Bringing plenty
To people of Misr
And far beyond her shores.

And harken, O Most Beloved
(So sings the storyteller),
But for the life-giving
Flow of the white river,
All would be desert —
Wind-whipped and dry —
Under the brazier sun of Misr.

POST CARD

Dear Stevie, and all,
The Red Sea is red!
     That's because of all
the red seaweed in it.
Next - if the wind and my
        map are right -
Balloon and I go over the
     Arabian Sea, to see
a bit of India.
Your friend,
        Koa Koala

To Master Steven Addison
℅ Mr. and Mrs. Addison
At Addison Cottage
Sydney, Australia 1113

The Sister Sits Dreaming

IN THE LARGEST HOUSE in our small village in India, there is soon to be a wedding.

The father of the house hurries about getting money enough for his daughter's dowry.

The mother rushes both here and there, readying clothes and linens to go with the daughter to her new home.

And the small brother runs his legs off on errands to be done before the wedding day.

But the sister — for whom all this rushing about is done — does no running.

Not she!

The sister sits at the doorway dreaming.

"Yesterday," says the father, dropping coins into the dowry box, "I sold all the rice we can spare, and today, our only charpoy —"

And still there is not money enough!

So off he goes, to sell his second bullock. Over the hookah, he will haggle with his friends for a good price.

"The saris and rugs are ready," says the mother, "and the sheets, and pots for cooking and for water —"

"What next?" asks the small brother, hoping his mother will say the wedding foods.

But, alas, she does not.

"Next," she says, ticking them off on her fingers, "the cups for drinking toasts, and chirags to light the wedding feast."

"How many cups?" asks the small brother.

"Tell the potter," the mother says, "to make us twenty, no — thirty-five, no — sixty cups will be needed for all our guests."

"So many cups!" thinks the small brother.

"So much to do!" thinks the mother.

"Still more money!" sighs the weary father.

But the sister, bah!

That sister does not run or worry her head.

Not she.

Day after day, she sits dreaming.

The men pass her, going to the fields.

The children, too, herding goats and sheep.

The women pass, carrying jugs of water.

And still she sits dreaming, that one!

At last, all is ready for the wedding.

The tea is measured, ready for steeping. The rice and dal are cooking. Even the lamb for the curry is simmering in the ghee.

Then, out of the largest house in our small village in India, the mother comes running.

"Go at once to the potter," she tells the small brother, "for the sixty cups have not come, nor the chirags to light the feast."

What a load that will be to carry!

And still the sister sits dreaming.

"Like a sacred cow she sits!" says the small brother, with a scowl.

Then off he goes — this time not running.

This time, instead, the small brother strolls slowly along. He even stops at the bazaar on his way to the pottery.

Such rich things are here, eh, Little Son?

Brass bowls from Jaipur, bells from Moradabad, rugs from Mirzapur, saris from Murshidabad — embroideries, and carvings of wood or ivory, and jewels such as a bride might wear.

With that, the small brother looks up.

The sky has turned to sunset!

Is it already too late to get the cups and chirags from the potter? Like a hind, the small brother runs from the crowded bazaar.

Straight to the pottery he goes, and yes! the potter is still at his work.

"We have — not — yet — our cups and chirags for the wedding — of my sister!" he pants.

"Never fear, Little Son," says the potter, "for all is ready in good time."

Into one basket, he counts the sixty cups.

In another, he heaps the tiny chirags.

What a load it is!

Now the small brother cannot run like a hind. No, he wends slowly home — dragging his feet in the dry, golden dust.

When he comes to the largest house in our small village in India, all is in an uproar.

The father is pacing the road.

The mother is wringing her hands.

The dogs are barking. And the small brother's friends are waiting to see what will happen to him for coming home so late.

The small brother himself is uneasy.

He is more uneasy when the mother — without a word of "I thank you, Little Son" — takes the basket of chirags into the house.

He is still more uneasy when the father takes up the basket of cups and stalks after her.

Outside the house, very tired and most uneasy, stands the small brother.

"I am like a beggar," he tells himself. "A beggar who dares not enter!"

All at once, the tears spring from his eyes and stream through the layer of golden dust on his face.

At that (may the god Ganesh be praised!) the sister — for whom all the trouble began —

raises herself from her dreaming, and glides to the side of the small brother.

"Little Brother," she says, "I thank you for all you have done for my wedding."

She bends her face to his.

Then she says, "Tomorrow, I go from this village to that of my husband. Happy as I shall surely be, I shall miss the father and the mother. But oh, most of all, Little Brother — most of all I shall miss you!"

Now the quick tears fall from her eyes and course down her cheeks.

At once, the small brother throws his arms around the middle of his sister, and she folds her arms around him.

Together, they weep just long enough to ease and warm their hearts. That done, they dry their eyes and their reddened noses.

Then the small brother who had run his legs off, and the sister who had sat dreaming all the while, go in, hand in hand, to meet with the father and mother of the house.

And behind them, the door of the largest house in our small village in India closes.

Softly it closes.

Pwish-sh-t, like that.

Cheetahs and Cheetals

In India, children like to play Cheetahs and Cheetals. Two teams, one of Cheetahs (leopards) and one of Cheetals (deer), stand back-to-back at the center line of a course about twelve feet long.

The "home" line for the Cheetahs is in front of them — about six feet away. The Cheetals, too, are facing their home line.

The leader stands beside the two teams.

He calls, "Chee-chee-chee-chee —"

Then suddenly, he finishes with either Chee-TAH, or Chee-TAL. If it is Cheetah that he says, the Cheetahs run for their home line — with the Cheetals trying to catch them. Any player who is caught is out of the game.

Next time — who knows — the leader may call on the Cheetals. And so the game goes, until almost all the players are out. The team with more players still in — wins.

Mr. Wicked

When hunting a tiger,
Don't ever say "tiger."
Should he hear
He might start
Hunting you —
With a terrible snarl
And a horrible leap!
All in all, quite
The best thing to do
Is to speak of him as
"Mr. Wicked," instead,
And to shoot when
You're saying it, too.

Lucky Seven

Seven small lizards
Have come to our house —
Tiki-tak, tiki-tak, tu —
They're catching the insects
That scamper about,
Stinging each other
Or you!

And off in a corner
And calling away —
Tokay and tokay, and tokay,
A big lizard tells us
His name seven times — so
Our house will be lucky
Today!

Thailand 95

Nitaya's Birthday Gifts

TODAY is a special day for Nitaya.

It is her birthday — and she is awake almost before the sun is up.

Not to look for packages from her family and friends, for that is not the way of birthdays in Thailand.

Instead, Nitaya watches happily as her mother makes tiny rice balls and spicy curry for the big, brassy birthday tray.

Still smiling, she carries her brother, small Nai Ti, out to the family compound.

"We will choose flowers for a gift for the spirit house," she tells him.

This they do. The bouquet of blue iris and yellow bougainvillea vine is so pretty that Nitaya is sure the spirits are happy.

"Bow to them, Nai Ti," she says.

And lifting her hands to her lips, Nitaya bows as solemnly as he.

Next she picks some plantain leaves to wash in the canal. But — what do you think — while she is doing that, Nai Ti tumbles into the water!

"*Mai pen rai*," she laughs, "never mind. We need our morning baths, anyway."

By the time she, and Nai Ti, and the leaves are shining clean, the canal is busy with loaded boats. Some are on their way to Bangkok, and some are bringing fresh fish and vegetables and fruit to the village.

Today, Nitaya is to choose the birthday fruits herself. She starts with papayas, pineapples, bananas, and juicy sum-o.

"*Nung, song, sam, see, har, hok,*" counts the vendor, adding up the price.

Nitaya has money enough, and more!

She asks for a big, spiny durian, too, and gives all her satangs to the vendor.

Then, "Thank you," says the vendor, and "Thank you," says Nitaya. And into the house she goes to help prepare the fruit.

The tray is a pretty sight when the plantain leaves are heaped with the many colored birthday foods!

Proudly, Nitaya carries it to the homes of all her family. When all her gifts are given — except for two — she takes them to the homes of her two best friends.

Chula is flying her kite.

But she stops to enjoy her gift.

Prasom is playing with her pet monkey, but she ties him to a tree, and comes to nibble at her gift, too.

"Where do you go for your birthday treat, Nitaya?" she asks.

"Yes, where?" asks Chula.

"To ride the elephant in the park!" Nitaya tells them. But before her friends can marvel at so wonderful a birthday treat, Nitaya's mother calls her.

"It is time for us to go to the temple," she says, holding out Nitaya's birthday gift for the priest.

But what do you think — just as Nitaya takes the tray, Nai Ti grabs one of the rice balls and stuffs it in his mouth!

He grabs some papaya, too.

"No, Nai Ti!" cries Nitaya.

Her mother laughs.

"*Mai pen rai,*" she says, "never mind. We will make another tray for the priest!"

Then she, Nitaya, and Nai Ti sit down and eat all the food on the tray, laughing at the way things have turned out.

Soon — with a fresh gift for the priest — all three set out for the temple.

Its bells tinkle in the breeze, and the priest himself comes out to receive Nitaya's birthday gift to him. He blesses her, too.

It is a solemn moment, and Nitaya thanks him with a soft and polite, "*Khob khun!*"

By now the sun is high.

Back at their house, Grandmother is waiting to care for Nai Ti while Grandfather takes Nitaya and her mother to Bangkok.

It is a long ride on the canal, and then on the river — but at last, Nitaya and her mother are in the city, and on their way to the park.

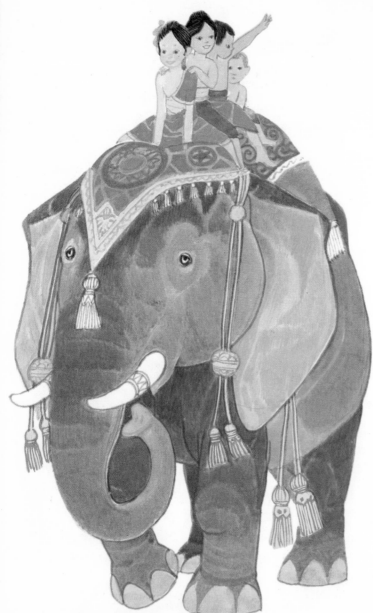

Now it is dusk, and time to go home.

Grandfather's sampan, loaded with goods he has bought at the market, is waiting in the river. So away they all go.

As the sky darkens, all the boats are lighted with small lanterns. It is such a pretty sight that Nitaya cannot speak — and still her birthday is not over.

At the compound, there is the sound of music so everyone can dance the ramwong in two big circles — one within the other.

There is the sweet-smelling night all around, and the chatter of Prasom's pet monkey, and the haughty meows of Mow — Nitaya's own coffee-and-cream colored pet.

And there is Nitaya's father — home from his work in the fields — waiting to dance, first with her pretty mother. And then (oh, the wonder of it!) to take Nitaya herself to the inner circle to dance round and round, until at last the stars fade, and her birthday is over — for this one year.

First comes the elephant ride.

High on its huge, gray back, Nitaya — and three other children — ride round and round and round and round the track.

After that, what do you think?

There is another treat — a walk along a path edged with shrubs all clipped to look like animals, and dancers, and a goddess with many arms.

And there is a visit to the zoo, and a small meal of rice and fish, eaten outdoors at the vendor's stall.

Last of all, there is even an ice with pink syrup — a special treat indeed!

Hoa Binh?

Small one,
You ask what peace is —
It means the end
Of shooting. In peace we
Can go back again
To our own village,
Build our own house.

In peace we can
Ride the water buffalo
To the rice fields,
Catch tilapia enough
To fill us full,
And play our games
Right to the end.

In peace there is
No more of running —
We can stay
To hear the storyteller
Spin out his whole tale,
And even watch all of
The Dragon Dance.

In peace,
We need only run
Laughing, to meet
Our father coming across
The growing rice fields —
If he comes home again —
In time of peace.

Chu Ling's Today

ONLY AT THE TIME of a festival is Chu Ling's family all together, and today is such a time.

His father and mother are home from work. And his much-older brother is home from school.

And his grandmothers — both of them, the mother of his father and the mother of his mother — are at the table, too.

Everyone is talking about things of little interest to six-year-old Chu Ling!

But he listens quietly while his brother talks about learning to speak French, and playing soccer when his school day ends.

And he tries hard to listen while his father speaks of something called The-increased-production-at-the-factory.

And while his mother speaks of How-much-better-things-are-in-the-New-China.

It is hard for Chu Ling to keep from wriggling, harder still for him to keep his eyes open.

All that grown-up talk makes him sleepy!

But at last the meal is over.

Chu Ling's Grandmother Chu, his father's mother, gives him some lichee nuts — and a smile.

His Grandmother Chen, his mother's mother, takes his hand and leads him off to the room where he sleeps.

"Would you like to sleep, Chu Ling? she asks. "Or would you like a story?"

"A story, please, honorable grandmother!" says Chu Ling. So they sit, face to face.

"A story," says his Grandmother Chen. "Yes, I shall tell you a story of long ago — when families lived together every day —"

"When clothes were in bright colors!" cries Chu Ling. "And houses were large, with flowers in the courtyards, and birds and fish —"

"Even so," says his grandmother. "The story will be of those times. For even today, my grandson, there is much to be learned from the ways and thoughts of the past."

So, with Chu Ling opening and chewing his lichee nuts as softly as he can, here is the story his Grandmother Chen tells to him.

The Girl Who Used Her Wits

In China, many and many years ago, there lived a woman who had two fine sons. When it came time for them to marry, they chose two pretty maidens from a far-away city.

Once the weddings were over, the two sons brought their young wives to be part of their mother's own household.

At first, the woman was more than happy with her pretty new daughters-in-law.

"They are well-mannered," she told her sons, "and as pretty as a cherry orchard in bloom."

To herself, the woman thought also that the young wives treated her like an empress.

She had only to think of a delicious cup of tea, and the girls set it before her!

It was so also with meals.

Nothing need she do but sit before her small red lacquered table — and in came her daughters-in-law with dainty bowls filled with all the foods she liked best.

"Oh yes," she thought, "my sons have taken the finest of wives to themselves."

But no sooner had the woman thought that, than in came the girls. Bowing low, they begged her permission to visit — for a short time — the city where their parents lived.

"Go and enjoy yourselves, my blossoms," the woman said generously.

And away went the two young girls.

Now while they were gone, they were greatly missed. The woman's sons moped about, longing for their beautiful wives to return.

As for the woman, how she missed the many things the girls had done for her!

"This must not happen again," she thought. And she soon devised a plan that would keep her sons' wives at her side.

Not long after the girls returned to her household, they again begged to go on a short visit to their old homes.

"Go you shall," said the woman. "But unless you bring back two gifts for which I long, you may never return to your husbands."

The girls promised to bring whatever she desired. Indeed, so eager were they to be off that they barely listened to her wishes.

"Lotus Blossom," said the woman, "you will most graciously bring me fire wrapped in a paper. And you, Peachbloom, may bring me wind in a paper."

Away went the girls, as happy as larks.

It was only when they were returning that they realized what they had promised.

"Fire wrapped in a paper!" said Lotus Blossom. "Never can I bring that — for the

thinking. Yet the maiden told them to be of good cheer.

After they had eaten, she came to them and said, "Lotus Blossom, you shall have fire in a paper to take to your mother-in-law."

So saying, she gave that young wife a pretty paper lantern with a lighted candle in it.

"It *is* fire in a paper!" Lotus Blossom marveled. "Now I can return, after all!"

Nodding, the young maiden turned to Peachbloom and fanned her cheek gently with a dainty paper fan.

"It is truly wind in a paper!" cried Peachbloom, taking the fan in astonishment.

At once, the two young wives — having thanked the young maiden with all their hearts — took their gifts and hurried toward home.

Their mother-in-law, seeing the gifts, supposed that the girls had wits as well as

fire would burn the paper to ashes!"

"No more than I can bring wind in a paper," cried Peachbloom. "Surely both would blow away!"

And, realizing that they could never return to their dear husbands, the young wives sat at the roadside weeping bitterly.

Soon a young maiden, riding on a water buffalo, stopped to try and comfort them.

"It will not do to weep," she said when she had heard of their sad situation. "To overcome ill fortune, you must use your wits."

This the young wives could not do.

So at last the young maiden took them up on the water buffalo with her, and took them to her humble home to eat and to rest.

When morning came, the young wives were red-eyed with weeping — instead of

WHEN GRANDMOTHER CHEN has finished the story, Chu Ling has many questions to ask her.

He wants to hear what the house was like, and what Lotus Blossom and Peach-bloom wore, and if there was—indeed—a small red lacquered table for the drinking of tea.

Once again, for she has answered these same questions many times, Grandmother Chen tells of the silken garments the young wives wore.

She tells of the great house with its many moon gates for looking out at the trees and flowers in the fragrant courtyards.

Before she comes to the red lacquered tea table, however, into the room come all the rest of the family — one by one.

Their loose shirts and trousers are of plain fabrics, all in one drab blue. And the room itself seems bare and drab to Chu Ling — after all he has just heard.

"What did you learn from the story your Grandmother Chen has told?" his father asks.

"To use my wits," says Chu Ling.

"No more than that?" asks his father.

"To — to obey also," Chu Ling says.

"Quite so," says his father. "All is planned in the New China — we have only to work hard and obey the orders given to us."

Chu Ling nods obediently.

"But in the New China," he says, "it is not so pretty as before. I would wish for a small red lacquered table for the drinking of tea."

"You would wish this," says his father, "although for every fine table in the homes

beauty and grace. Most graciously, she received them again into her household.

And since the girls were overjoyed to be back with their husbands, they thought twice before jaunting off to their old homes again.

Day in and day out, they served their mother-in-law as prettily as before.

And in the evenings, they sat contentedly in the courtyard with their husbands — listening to the sweet, wistful song of a nightingale who came to sing in the wisteria vine which climbed the wall of their new home.

Hopscotch in China

CHU LING AND HIS FRIENDS like to play hopscotch. Their game course looks like the one in the picture.

Each player starts at Home.

On two feet, he jumps to Box 7, then 6, 5, 4, 3, 2, and 1.

Next, on his right foot, he hops from Box 1 to Box 2 — and so on — to Home. From there, still on his right foot, he hops to Box 7, to 6, 5, 4, 3, 2, and 1.

Then, the hardest one! On his left foot, he hops from 1, to 3, to 5, to 7 — and Home.

If he can't make a box, or steps on a line between boxes — out he goes.

Another player takes his place, and tries to be the last one to go out.

of the rich, there were a thousand families who had no food to eat?"

"Today," adds his mother, "all may eat."

What can Chu Ling say to that?

He can say nothing. Very glad he is that it is now time to stroll in the park, and talk with friends, and choose a picnic spot.

"The park is beautiful," Chu Ling whispers to Grandmother Chen as they stand admiring a great mass of yellow chrysanthemums.

"Yes, Chu Ling," she sighs. "And when you are grown — and all have food enough — there may be time in the New China for more of beauty such as this."

"If I work hard and obey?" asks Chu Ling.

"Yes," says Grandmother Chen, sighing again.

"And perhaps," she whispers in a voice as soft as the falling of a single petal, "if you use your wits, as well — you may someday drink your tea at a small red lacquered table all carved with dragons, as in the story of China long ago."

Good Morning!

In the small, clear pool,
Hai! The fish nose up, skimming
The crumbs I bring them.

On the Bamboo Hill

SLOWLY, SLOWLY — so slowly today — we climb up the Bamboo Hill.

Here the trees grow thick, slender, and tall. In summer, their many-fingered leaves reached for hot sunlight, and cast cool shade.

Here we rested in thick-springing grass.

And heard light birdsong.

Sometimes a thin breeze turned the leaves, and lifted our damp, hot hair.

Here on the Bamboo Hill, we listened to many stories told by our most honorable grandfather, our Ojii-san.

Sometimes we watched as slender bamboo trees were cut down — only a few, here and there.

Hak! Hak! Hak!

Down they came, falling lightly.

From their slender golden trunks, many useful things would be made—baskets, fishing rods, lanterns and fans, brushes for our painting pans, water spouts.

It is true.

Our most honorable grandfather, Ojii-san, said so in summer on the Bamboo Hill.

"Ai, and bamboo shoots to eat," he said once, sniffing the air for the drifting fragrance of our evening meal.

Then he rose up, leaning a little on his bamboo walking stick.

And we rose, too, to walk with him.

Down the Bamboo Hill we went, wondering if there would be bamboo shoots — as well as fish and rice — to eat that night.

That was in full summer.

Today, the sun slants thinly as we go slowly, slowly down the hill again.

Tomorrow, when we wake, it will be time to go back to our own home in Tokyo.

And back again — so soon — to school!

POST CARD

Dear Deer, and Herd,

Japan has the fastest train in the entire world. It streaks at 130 miles an hour. Not even you- with Dingo after you -could go that fast. You should see it!
Greetings from Your Friend Koa Koala

To Deer and His Herd
In the Southern Mountains,
Australia 2003

Summer Homework

TODAY IN TOKYO, Mariko and her mother are shopping in a big store on the Ginza.

They buy new white blouses to go with Mariko's school jumpers. And a new school-bag for her books and papers and brushes.

And a new, clean notebook to write in.

"We must look at tatami, too," Mariko's mother says. "Those in your brother's room are no longer fit to be used."

Mariko nods and smiles.

But really, she wishes the shopping would be over — so she could go up to the roof of the store. Up there, there are many rides, such as one sees at a carnival.

Best of all, there is a Ferris wheel.

When you ride on that, up and around and down, you can see the rooftops of Tokyo!

At last the shopping is finished.

"I am almost certain of that," Mariko's mother says. "Now you may have your ride on the Ferris wheel."

So up they go, and Mariko gets on the Ferris wheel at last. From the top, she can see a little vendor and his tiny traveling

Japan 107

restaurant far down on the street below.

"I am so hungry, Mother-san," she says, as soon as the splendid ride is over.

"And I!" says her mother. "Shopping seems to make one wish for food!"

Soon they are both eating sweet little shrimp and rice, with a lovely hot sauce.

Never has it tasted so good!

And then, Mariko's mother says that they must ride home in a taxi.

"With so many packages," she says, "we could not go by bus."

Now, when her mother says "packages," Mariko remembers that she also has an important purchase to make.

"The little bowl for the fish from Ojii-san's pool!" she says. "Must we not choose that before we go home?"

"We must," her mother agrees.

So, loaded with parcels, Mariko and her

mother go to a small shop that sells such things. It does not take Mariko long to choose exactly the right bowl. She pays for it herself, and carries it most carefully.

At home, Mariko's brother helps her to catch the goldfish with a little net, and to put it in its shining new home.

Mariko adds a bit of water plant.

A pretty sight it is — the orange-gold of the fish and yellow-green of the plant!

"Your summer homework does you credit, Mariko," says her brother. "Now come, if you please, and see mine."

Ichiro has taken shells, from a day at the beach, and mounted them on a thin board.

Each one is labeled.

And Ichiro has written a paper about his collection of shells as well.

"It is splendid, Ichiro-san!" Mariko says.

At once, she gets her brushes and makes

a label for her fish. It says "Fish from the pool of my grandfather, Ojii-san, with whom we spent the last part of summer vacation."

The label is beautiful.

But it is too big for the small bowl!

"It could be done as a scroll," says Mariko's father. And so it could.

Tired as she is — the day has been long — Mariko letters the characters on a long strip of rice paper. She rolls it into a scroll.

And her mother ties the scroll with a bit of thread — orange-gold like the fish. It is easy for Mariko to tape this to the bowl.

"Now it's ready," she says. "I thank you all for taking time to help me."

So tired is Mariko by now, that she goes straight to her own room.

She puts the fish bowl on her small, low chest, and her jumper and new school blouse right beside it.

Her bed is already spread on the floor.

Soon Mariko is tucked in, ready for sleep.

But first, she wants to remember Ojii-san helping her to catch the little fish in the pool at the foot of the Bamboo Hill.

Mariko smiles, remembering that.

Next, she wants to wonder what kind of summer homework her classmates will bring to school tomorrow.

And what she will tell about hers.

But before she can do that, Mariko's eyes have closed — all by themselves.

Mariko is sound asleep.

So hush, goes the tail of her small fish as it swims around in its shining bowl.

Hush, goes the flowering quince as its branches blow softly against the wall of Mariko's quiet house.

And high in the sky, the early fall moon peeps through the sliding door and shines softly on Mariko all through the night.

Good Night!

See how the white moon rises,
Edging the scudding clouds
With polished light!

No Time For Splashdowns!

THE EARLY FALL is not a peaceful time in the South Pacific Ocean.

It is a time of sudden squalls.

And even typhoons.

Then the howling winds whip the waves up into towering mountains of gray water, with deep, deep wet valleys in between.

Small ships are tossed about like straws.

Even great liners and freighters roll and wallow in the heavy seas until everyone aboard — except perhaps the captain — is sure that the next wave will turn them upside down.

This would be no time for astronauts to make a splashdown in the South Pacific!

Nor do they.

No flights are scheduled. For if they were, the aircraft carrier waiting for the capsule to come down would be tossed wildly in the storm.

The lookouts would look in vain, barely able to see two feet in front of them. And the frogmen, waiting to help the astronauts out of their capsule, would despair of ever getting near enough — in such a sea!

Even the astronauts, listening to weather reports on the radio, would be uneasy.

Who would know better than they that their drogue parachutes would be whipped and twisted by the fierce winds?

Or that their capsule — after splashdown — would bob in the water like a helpless cork?

Or that, in such a sea, the rescue helicopters could never catch them to take them to the aircraft carrier — and safety?

No one would know these things better than the astronauts. Except the many men who plan and arrange their flights into space.

They know what to expect in early fall.

And so they plan each flight for a time

when the weather should be fine for a safe splashdown.

In summer, yes.

In spring and winter, sometimes.

But never and never in early fall — the time of sudden squalls, and even howling typhoons, in the wide stretch of water called the South Pacific Ocean!

POST CARD

Dear Kookaburra, and all,
Wish I'd planned my flight
   as Well as Aerospace
     chaps!
Balloon was just looking
chipper, when we hit a
typhoon. It is to be hoped
that someone in Mexico
will have blue, yellow, and
    red paint to spare!
Your dismayed
   friend, Koa Koala

To Kookaburra
Up Around Toowoomba
Australia 1123

The South Pacific 111

La Suerte

ALL SUMMER, José and his parents had been riding north in a crowded truck.

They stopped wherever a farmer had a crop that was ready to be picked.

And there they stayed for a few days.

José's mother and father picked strawberries, or tomatoes, or asparagus all day long. And José waited at the end of each row to do the sorting and packing.

Very careful work that was!

Big strawberries had to be put in one basket and small ones in another.

The same with tomatoes. And with the asparagus, each bunch had to be of stalks of the same thickness.

José had learned well.

"*Bueno*, José," his father would say, "you work quickly — it is good."

"Not everyone can handle the tender crops," his mother would add. "It takes special care and skill to do this."

Then José's chest would puff out with pride. "And it pays well," he would say, making his fingers work even faster — and more carefully.

At the end of each day, the family would have a quick supper. Then — most of the time — José would fall into bed, and sleep as if he had never slept before!

Every few nights, he and his family slept in a different camp. Most of the time, the camp was clean enough. And comfortable enough — for a migrant camp.

Mr. Fernandez, el patrón, saw to that. He was proud of the work done by his crew.

Still, sometimes a camp was bad.

"Remember the farm of Mr. Sickles?" José's mother sometimes said with a shudder. "Such dirt! I wept through that night!"

"But one night only!" his father would remind her. "We do not stay long in such bad camps, do we, José?"

112   *Mexico*

"No," José would say, munching away on a good supper of chili and corn cakes.

Tonight, even his mother was happy.

For tonight they had come to a good camp — in a good town. There was even to be a party for the migrant workers.

So everyone washed until he shone, and dressed himself in his best clothes.

Then shyly, the workers piled into el patrón's truck and bounced and jounced into town.

No one was shy for long.

The people of this town were so friendly that even José's shy mother was soon dancing. His father — never shy — played his guitar and sang along with it.

And José — not wanting to miss anything — watched, and listened, and smiled.

"There is room in our school for visiting children," a pretty lady said to him. "Could you go while you're here?"

Now José did not like school anywhere.

So he ducked his head and said, "No, Señorita, I must work with my family —"

But, *madre mia!* his father had heard.

"He can be spared, Señorita," he said in his great, booming voice. "Certainly yes, to have schooling — you hear, José?"

So that was how it happened that José went to school for two whole weeks.

At first, he grumbled a bit.

"The work is hard, Padre," he said.

"You go anyway!" his father cried. "You like this town — the fine homes, the shops, the people, yes?"

"Yes," sniffed José.

"Then go to school and learn all you can," his father said. "One day, you may be a

great man and live in such a town!"

"OK," said José.

"Not OK!" his father shouted. " 'Yes, Padre' — and now hang your head and go to your bed!"

After that, José really listened when he was in the school. He began to ask questions — and get splendid answers from the teacher, too.

The time flew. All at once, he had only three more days to go to that school.

"Only three days!" whispered José.

Now that he had begun to learn, he thought that he could never learn enough!

"I would like to go to this school always," he told his teacher on the very last day.

"You will go to school in Mexico, José?" she asked — rumpling his hair.

"Every day, Señorita!" José said.

"Good," said the teacher. "And I will be glad when you come back here next year."

Next year was a thing to think about!

José thought about it often, riding home on the bouncing, jouncing truck.

"Next year, I will surprise her with all I have learned," he told himself. "And the year after that —even more!"

Softly, José began singing.

His father, happy because his son now wanted to go to school and become a great man, strummed his guitar and sang, too.

José's mother joined in, and presently, everyone in the truck was singing away.

"Sing happy!" called el patrón, from the driver's seat. "This year we have had la suerte — our pockets will be full all through the winter. Our stomachs as well!"

Then he began to sing, too.

The people in the truck in back took up the tune. And the people in the truck in back of *that* truck began singing, too.

They made a happy sound in the countryside as they bounced and jounced towards their homes in Mexico.

On The Coffee Hills

On the hills in Costa Rica, the small coffee trees are grown. They grow in the shade of larger trees — for so do the plump coffee cherries ripen gently to brilliant red.

Every day, the trees must be tended.

Sometimes — bending and stooping — a family will set out new, young plants.

Sometimes they will prune the branches of older trees. And always, they must cut away the brush that would crowd the coffee trees.

Day by day, some cherries ripen.

Everyone helps with the picking. Even small Luisa can pick carefully.

The ripe cherries are spread on a bed of leaves, or cloth, to dry.

A big brother turns them to dry evenly.

From time to time, the father may call, "Hola! Come along, little ones! Have you fallen asleep? Bring more ripe cherries for us to dry!"

One day, there are dried cherries enough to take into the village. Basket after basket is loaded into the family's wagon.

And such a wagon it is — all painted in its own pretty designs, in soft, faded colors!

And, as it rumbles down the hill to the village, it sings its own special creaking tune.

When the coffee — that precious coffee — has been unloaded at the beneficio, the father is paid for it.

Now the family can go to the market to buy the few things needed at home.

And to look at the many things for sale — baskets and woven cloth, fresh vegetables and fruits, even live chickens!

Best of all, they can meet with friends.

The father talks of the price of coffee.

The mother talks of family things.

The children shout at their games.

At last the day in the village ends. The family piles into its wagon again, to ride back to the hills in the quiet dusk.

As to the coffee — that precious coffee — already the skin and pulp of the cherries is being washed away at the beneficio. Out drop the twin coffee beans, to be washed and dried.

One day, packed in large bags, they will be sent to countries all over the world — wherever people like coffee.

"The best coffee in the world!" the father may say as the wagon jogs homeward.

And so it is, the coffee of Costa Rica.

A thing to make a family proud!

Tomorrow morning, everyone — even the small, sleeping Luisa — will be busy in the hills again, tending the coffee trees that pay for all the things the family needs.

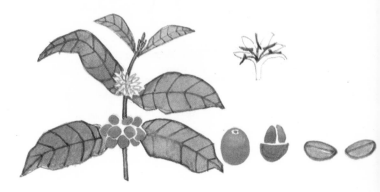

For Me — Si?

Thwacking
And swinging
And thwacking again,
Shiny machetes are
Cutting the cane.
Most is for sugar
But I need some, too,
It's so lovely
And sticky
And tasty
To chew!

The Greedy Wife

THERE WAS ONCE a thin, thin husband who had a fat, fat wife. Yet, every day when the husband came home from work, the wife would place only one small, green salad on the table.

"Eat your dinner, my husband," she would say. "As for me, I am not hungry."

Still she grew fatter and fatter!

The husband wondered how that could be. So, one day, instead of going to work in the fields, he crept under the house. He made a hole in the floor, and, putting his eye to it, watched his wife the whole day.

Soon the fat wife filled a big bowl with bread crumbs, and fresh milk, and sugar.

Click, click, click went her spoon as she gobbled up that big, hearty breakfast.

"I am still hungry," she sighed.

So, for lunch, she made herself a vast omelet topped with ripe peppers and big juicy tomatoes.

Click, click, click went her fork as she ate up every bite.

For a bit, the fat wife dozed in her chair.

Then she awakened, hungry all over again.

Now, as it was pouring and teeming rain, she went through the house to the chicken coop. There she killed a fine, fat hen to stew.

Click, click, click went her fork and spoon as she gobbled that — sauce, potatoes, and all.

When it was nearing time for her husband to come home, the fat wife washed and put away all the dishes she had used. Then she made a small, green salad for the poor man's supper.

In he came, as dry as a bone in spite of the pouring and teeming rain.

"How can you be dry when you have been working in all this rain?" asked his greedy wife.

"Ah, wife," said the husband. "The rain was as fine as the crumbs you ate for breakfast. But, being clever, I took shelter under a tree with leaves as broad as the omelet you ate for lunch. If I hadn't, I should be as wet

as the chicken in sauce which you had for dinner —"

Hearing this, the wife blushed red as a pepper. Quickly, she killed another fat hen and cooked it for her husband's supper.

And, from that day to this, the wife never again ate by herself. She cooked one fine meal for both to eat when her husband came home.

So it was that the husband, too, grew as fat as she, and both grew jolly. And now, *colorín colorado,* their story is ended.

In The Rain Forest

LOOK, TODAY IN THE RAIN FOREST, the light is cool and green as underwater. The great fern trees rise up, with slow drops falling from their fronds to the damp-smelling forest floor.

What shall we do first in this secret place?

Shall we listen to birds that whistle and screech as they dart, bright-feathered, from tree to vine to tree?

Or try to catch — and hold — just one of all the tiny chameleons that live here?

It can't be done.

Zipp-p-p! They disappear in a swift, slender flash of quivering emerald green.

Well then, we'll hunt for a mongoose.

Teeth bared, he backs away to hide — his ferret eyes searching the green-gloom for the slither of a gliding snake.

But look, the flowers of the rain forest can't run away! What if we find a spray of little yellow orchids, hovering on their stem like a flight of butterflies?

Or see a nest of air plants — like giant, garnet dahlias — bright in the green-gloom?

That is a sight to tell about!

But hush, the stream is tumbling down the mountainside! They say it brings with it bits of real, shining gold.

Let's catch ourselves a hat full!

Just think of all we can buy back in San Juan — to eat, and play with, and show to everyone. We'll strut like roosters then — and never tell how we grew rich.

Don't ever tell.

It will be our secret.

And the secret, too, of El Yunque, who keeps the rain forest on its steep slope. And wears a crown of heavy clouds — as if it were one of the Three Kings, bearing gifts of shining gold, and jewels, and sweet-smelling myrrh.

POST CARD

Dear Cassowary, and Chums,
We are on our way to
South America if the wind
over the Caribbean Sea
holds steady on.
Are you getting my cards?
Hope so!
I've made up zip code
numbers for everywhere
in Australia, just
to make sure.
Adios, Amigos, from
Koa Koala

To Cassowary and Chums
Hither and Yon in
Australia 2000, etc.

BRAZIL 50

Minha Direita Desocupada

IN THIS BRAZILIAN GAME, six or more players form a circle — leaving an empty space.

Each player chooses for himself the name of a person, animal, or flower.

He tells everyone his name.

In playing, the girl or boy to the left of the empty place calls out *"Minha direita desocupada!"* (In English, that would be "There's an empty place at my right!") Then he says, "Come and fill it, Burro!"

That's if someone has chosen that name. Now "Burro" must hurry to that place.

If he is too slow, he is out of the game, and must pay a forfeit to be in again.

The Fabulous Hat

ON PLEASANT DAYS in San José — a city in Bolivia — Niña and her mother always went to choose the fresh vegetables for their evening meal.

And this Niña loved to do.

This was not because she liked walking to the market. Nor because she was unusually fond of vegetables — for she was not.

It was because her mother bought the vegetables from an Indian woman who wore the most fabulous hat.

The hat was black.

It had a high crown with a splendid band around it, and a small, stiff brim.

And Niña, who was unusually fond of hats, wondered where such a hat could be bought.

Often, she asked her mother.

"But Niña," her mother always said, "such hats are worn only by Indians who live far up in the mountains of Bolivia."

Niña's mother was saying that today.

But today, Niña was not listening.

For by now, they were but half a block away from the Indian with the fabulous hat.

And something was wrong!

The woman — quite old she seemed to Niña — had not tied her llama strongly enough.

So down the street it came, vegetable baskets and all, running away. After it came the Indian woman, and her husband, and her two daughters, and her one small son.

But the llama was far ahead of them.

It was sure to get away, unless something was done at once!

Now, besides being fond of hats, Niña was exceptionally fond of animals. She carried with her — wherever she went — a few treats for any animals she might meet.

Corn for pigeons. Sugar for horses. A dog biscuit, in case of meeting a dog.

And bits of lettuce for a llama.

Niña had fed this particular llama so many times that it was, by now, kindly disposed toward her. It even seemed to know her voice.

So, when she called, "Come, Llama!" the llama slowed down a bit.

When she held out the lettuce, it stretched out its neck to sniff at it.

And when Niña said, "It's for you, Llama!" the animal stopped in its tracks and began to eat from her hand.

Presently, up came the Indian woman.

Up came her husband.

Up came her two daughters.

Up came her one small son.

"Our thanks, Señorita Niña," they all said. "You have stopped our llama. You have saved our vegetables that we brought all the way to the market to sell!"

The Indian woman said something more.

She said, "We would wish also to do something for you. What might it be, Señorita?"

"Well," said Niña (taking great care *not* to look at her mother), "I have long wished for a fabulous hat such as yours. Perhaps you will tell me where one can be bought?"

"Aha!" said the Indian woman, spreading her arms wide. "Why buy, Señorita?"

With that, she said something (in Indian) to her husband, who said something (in Indian) to his first daughter, who said something (still in Indian) to his second daughter.

That daughter said, "Aha!" and looked at her small brother.

She took the hat, exactly like the mother's but much smaller, from her brother's head.

Down the line it went, from the small boy's head to the second daughter, to the first daughter, to the husband, and to the Indian woman herself.

She — with a happy smile — clapped the hat directly on Niña's head.

It was a perfect fit!

"It is yours, Señorita Niña," she said.

"*Muchas gracias!*" said Niña, wishing she were standing in front of her own mirror at that very moment.

So that is why — in spite of what her mother had said — that particular kind of fabulous hat is not worn *only* by Indians who come down from the mountains of Bolivia.

Such a hat is worn also by a small girl who lives in San José, a fairly large Bolivian city. It is worn morning, noon, and night — everywhere really, except to bed and at the table — by the Señorita Niña, herself.

Bolivia 121

The Grand Don Carlos

"Look here!" cried Juan's father, rushing into the house with a letter in his hand, "the Señor and Señora — and the small Don Carlos — are coming to the estancia tomorrow!"

"Tomorrow!" gasped Juan's mother. "So little time to make things ready! Come, Juan, you will help — perhaps polish the floors —"

Then "Estrella!" she called, "Rosita! Drop what you are doing. Come with me to the big house, to make everything clean and fresh!"

So away they ran, Juan and his mother, and the two chambermaids, to open the big house.

When Juan saw the main room (as big as a corral!) filled with fine furnishings and soft rugs, his eyes opened wide.

"It is *grande!*" he whispered.

"No, no," said his mother. "You have not seen *grande* until you have seen the Señor's house in Buenos Aires! But come, to work —"

Off she went, with an armload of fresh linen, while Juan worked on the floors.

The farther into the house he went, the more he wondered at its richness. What could the house in the city be like?

"And what," he wondered, "will the Señor and Señora — and Don Carlos — be like?"

Very grand, Juan was sure!

On the next morning, when he heard automobiles coming, he ran out of his own small house.

"They come, Madre!" he called, staring at three long, shiny autos that were pulling up in front of the big house.

Two were piled with bags, and — most likely, Juan supposed — with the Señora's many servants.

But out of the first, and biggest auto, stepped the Señor (himself not so big or grand), and the Señora (not so pretty as Juan's own mother) and the young Señor.

Well, he was grand enough!

He was taller than Juan, though of the same age, and such clothes he wore!

Not a rip or patch anywhere!

When Don Carlos saw Juan staring, he smiled and came straight to meet him.

"I am Carlos," the boy said. "Will you show me the estancia, please? Especially, I should like to see my father's horses."

Juan could hardly answer.

His mouth felt dry and numb.

"Perhaps the cattle, too?" he asked.

But no, Don Carlos cared not for them. So Juan led him to the stable where the fine riding horses were being curried.

Don Carlos whistled.

"Each is *mas bonitas*, si?" he asked, standing legs apart and proud.

"No," squeaked Juan. "Guarani is *mas bonitas!*"

He pointed to the great brown stallion.

It was standing still to be curried, but the eyes of Guarani were rolling.

"Si!" said Don Carlos. "*Mas bonitas* — I shall ride Guarani while I am here."

Juan had to smother a laugh.

"No one rides Guarani except my father," he said. "This horse is a wild one — no one else can handle him."

Don Carlos tossed his head.

"Take me to your father, then," he said.

Juan did so, and standing back a little, he tried not to listen to their talk. So all he heard was the murmer of voices, and all he saw was his father shaking his head.

Don Carlos stamped his foot.

Juan's father shrugged.

He had Guarani saddled — it took two gauchos to do that — and brought to him.

Juan drew in his breath.

But it was not Don Carlos who mounted the horse. It was Juan's father.

"You will watch, please, Don Carlos!" he called, and then he was off.

Such strength he had with the reins, and with his knees! Guarani, eyes afire, tried to shake his rider — but could not.

He reared and bucked, and stopped so

suddenly that anyone — except Juan's father — would have gone over his head.

Then, seeing that he could not throw his rider, Guarani shot off at a gallop. But not once, while Juan and Don Carlos watched, did the stallion get the upper hand.

Juan's father made him obey his every command.

"It is *magnifico!*" whispered Don Carlos. "Your father is a superb horseman!"

Then he looked away, and looked not quite comfortable, either.

"And only think, Juan," he stammered. "I supposed I could ride Guarani. Not even my father could handle that horse!"

Now Don Carlos began to laugh — and he was laughing at himself.

He laughed so hard that, try as he did, Juan could not help joining in. No longer did his mouth feel dry and numb. Don Carlos was not so grand as to be frightening, after all.

Shyly, Juan smiled at him.

And Don Carlos smiled back. "I am most thirsty, Juan," he said.

"Then come," Juan told him. "My mother will make mate for you to drink."

"For us both?" asked the young señor.

"*Si, amigo!*" Juan said.

And together the two walked toward Juan's tiny house — letting the grand big house wait until Don Carlos had sipped mate with his new friend Juan.

POST CARD

Dear Dingo, and All,

Chile is amazing! Ice and
   snow thunder down
El Tronador, <u>fundos</u> bloom
with everything from beans
to flax, and there are
     even rain forests.
In Santiago, the <u>carabineros</u>
change guard.
    A splendid sight!
Your amazed
   friend, Koa Koala

To Dingo and All

Here and There in

Australia 1002, etc.

The Terrible Cape

Oh, it's best to beware
When you're rounding Cape Horn!
Any sailor may wish
That he'd never been born,
As his ship groans
And strains in the cold
And the gray of the waves
From two oceans coming his way,
And the winds from two oceans
A-blowing away!

There are treacherous rocks,
There are ships, wrecked and torn,
There is cold — bitter cold
That can barely be born —
So it's best to beware
When you're rounding Cape Horn,
When you're rounding
The terrible, awesome, unbearable
Tip of bare land that is known
As Cape Horn.

Yes, beware when you're
Rounding Cape Horn!

The Coldest Place

In December, it is summer in Antarctica.

Not that it is warm then.

By no means!

It is always bitter cold near the South Pole — colder even than in the barren wastes of the far North, where lies the North Pole.

Still, in Antarctica, summer *is* warmer.

The days grow longer. The sun shines, warming the vast ice-clad waters. And the harsh, deep ice on those waters begins to break. The ice groans and moans. It pushes up into icy ridges and hills.

Suddenly, CRACK! A ridge breaks into ice floes that bob in the gray, icy waters.

Now a ship or two may try to plow its way to Antarctica. Slowly, cautiously, it moves forward, picking its way through the bobbing floes.

When the ship makes land safely, its cargo is unloaded — new supplies for the

men who are exploring the still uncharted, frigid land.

And mail — mail from home — is brought to the men working here. Out of their ice tunnels they come, to open every barrel and crate, and to share all the news from their homes.

Their voices ring out above the endless shrill of the wind, and the endless cracking of the ice.

In summer, too, the voices of animals are heard again in Antarctica.

The cry of the skua gull diving for fish.

The barks and yelps of seals, as they plunge and swim in the icy waters. When they yelp in terror, it means that the killer whale is hunting for them — and too close by, at that!

In summer, too, the Adelie penguins come to the Antarctic ice cap. Croaking excitement, they waddle to their rookery to choose their mates and raise new families of fuzzy chicks.

When an egg is laid, the father and mother penguin take turns keeping it warm. First the father holds the egg on his feet and warms it with his thick breast feathers.

Then the mother, having eaten and rested, tends the egg while the father has his fish.

At last the eggs are hatched.

The tiny chicks must still be kept warm in the Antarctic cold. As they grow, they learn to huddle together, their bodies making patches of warmth in the snow and wind.

Finally, the chicks are big enough to wander about as they wish — poking their bills into everything they see. They are soon following the explorers on their rounds.

"What's going on?" they seem to ask, as the men test the depth of the ice, or survey and map parts of the ice-clad continent, or watch and study the ways of the animals that come here.

The curious chicks, and their parents, soon make friends with the explorers.

They gobble the food the men offer them, and watch carefully as the men play baseball or football in the deep, crisp snow.

In turn, the men watch the penguin's games — games of follow-the-leader, and coasting down hills on their sleek bellies, and splashing into the water to race one another round and round.

Slowly, but all too soon, the Antarctic summer ebbs away.

Days grow shorter.

Nights stretch out, colder and longer.

Day after day, the Adelie penguins take to the water to go to their winter home in the north.

A day comes when the last of the penguins are ready to leave.

The explorers watch and call goodbye.

They watch and watch, until these last penguins are no more than bobbing dots in the vast waters.

Then, with a sigh, the men return to their work.

It will be a long, lonely, and bitter cold time until summer — and the Adelie penguins — return to visit the barren shores of Antarctica again!

About Wise, Wicked Spider

IN COMPOUNDS IN GHANA, the day's work ends as the sun sinks down. Mothers put away their weaving, and grandfathers their basketry.

Fathers come home from the fields.

And the evening meal is ready.

Always, there is fu-fu cooked over the open fires. Sometimes there will be palm oil sauce as well, or big chunks of tasty meat.

When everyone has eaten, the fun begins.

Drums beat out old rhythms for stories told by the movements of the dancers.

There may be the reciting of stories, too.

When there is, everyone listens in silence. But if — by some splendid chance — the story is about Spider, laughter soon breaks the silence. For who can resist laughing at that wise, wicked fellow and his friends?

One story about them is told on the next few pages of this book. If you enjoy it as much as Ghanians do, you may want to borrow a whole book of stories about Spider from the library.

There is such a book, told by Joyce Cooper Arkhurst — who gathered the stories in the fire-and-starlight of Ghana itself.

Why Spider Lives In Ceilings

as told by Joyce Cooper Arkhurst

ONCE UPON A TIME the rainy season came to the forest, as it must come every year. But this time there was more rain than ever before.

Nobody had seen anything like it.

At night the water fell with a roar like thunder. In the morning it beat against the branches of the trees and tore their leaves from them.

It pounded against the thatched roofs of the villages and rushed about the footpaths. Little girls set pots under the sky to catch the water and ran back slipping and sliding.

The small, friendly rivers became deep and wide, and covered the sides of their banks. During the darkness the people fastened their doors and did not even look outside, for they could hear nothing but rain, rain, rain.

The animals in the forest, too, were

frightened by all the water. Hare could not find meadows of grass for his dinner. Elephant could not walk through the trees to chew the young branches. Tortoise could not crawl slowly along the earth to catch insects; and Spider, who had been too lazy to plant his farm or to set his fish traps, had nothing at all to eat.

Worst of all, the great Leopard, who hunts at night, was hungry, and had to stalk the forest during the day.

One afternoon, after many days, the rain stopped. Spider set out at once to look for something to eat. He went down the wide path that led to the river. Leopard went hunting, too, with a hungry look in his eye. He walked quietly on his four soft feet along the path that led to the river. That is how it happened that Spider and Leopard walked right into each other.

Now usually, Leopard loves a fat and juicy supper. He never thinks of anything as puny as Spider. But today he thought even Spider would taste good, and so he stopped to chat and tried to look friendly.

"Good afternoon, Mr. Spider," said Leopard. "How do you fare in all this wet weather?"

Now Spider was lazy and very naughty, but he was not stupid. He knew at once that Leopard's voice was much too sweet.

"I am well, Mr. Leopard, but I am in a great hurry," he answered. And with that, Spider jumped behind a great palm leaf, and Leopard could not find him no matter how he tried.

Leopard was so angry. He roared a roar that echoed against the hills. He sharpened his claws and his eyes turned green.

"Never mind," he thought after a few minutes, "I will go to Spider's house. I will hide behind his door and wait for him to come back. Then I will eat him, and if he brings any food, I will eat that, too."

Leopard went up the path from the river.

He went into Spider's little house, which was made of banana leaves. There he made himself into a round ball. He put his nose on his great paws, and sat down to wait.

Haven't I already told you that Spider was not stupid? He guessed exactly what Leopard would do. And so he took some time to think how he would handle the matter.

First, he went to the river and caught some fish left in the traps by people. Then he went to the farm and ate a cassava. For it is the custom that a hungry man may help himself to as much food as he needs; and no one will mind.

When he had enough to eat, Spider spent the afternoon looking for all his friends. He stayed away from his house as long as he could.

Finally, it began to get dark.

The sky filled with clouds, and once again the rain began to fall.

At last Spider *had* to go home.

So he went up the path that led past the river, and near his little house made of banana leaves.

Spider looked at the earth to see if Leopard had left any tracks. He listened to see if Leopard made any sound. He saw and he

heard nothing. Still, he knew the ways of Leopard, and he decided to try something else.

So he kept walking down the path, humming to himself, just as if he were thinking about nothing. Suddenly, he cried out:

"Ho! My banana-leaf house!"

Nobody answered. Everything was silent. Spider walked a little nearer. Still there was silence. Nobody said anything.

"That's funny," said Spider loudly, "my little house always answers me when I call her. I wonder what is wrong."

Once again, with all his might, he shouted, "Ho! My banana-leaf house. How are you?"

And from deep inside the house came a small, high voice. "I am fine, Mr. Spider. Come on in."

Then Spider burst out laughing.

"Now I know where you are, Mr. Leopard, and you shall never catch me," he said.

And with that, he ran quick as a flash through the window, and up to the highest corner of the ceiling. Leopard could not catch him although he tried and tried.

Spider was warm and dry and safe in the ceiling. I suppose that is why he decided to live there. And he is living there still.

Ashanti Chief

In Accra, at the library,
I can sit on an Ashanti stool
All painted red —
To look at picture books.

Then I am Ashanti chief,
And everyone in this big room
Must bow his head
In my royal presence.

At home, I will make umbrella
To walk beneath, and drums to say,
"He comes, the great
And warrior chief — bow down!"

In Accra, at the library,
I can sit on an Ashanti stool
All painted red,
And learn of many things!

Gorilla Gorilla Beringei

Gorilla gorilla beringei
On Visoke's slopes lives he,
As black as the night,
As tall as a man,
And he weighs (you'll never
Believe it, Sir!) he weighs
Four hundred and three!

Gorilla gorilla beringei
He beats his chest in glee,
And he quickly gobbles
The Galium vine,
And the fruit (the almost
Inedible fruit!) that grows
On the Pygeum tree.

Gorilla gorilla beringei
If ever you chance to see
Him — face to face —
In some mountain place,
Don't be alarmed, for he —
(Big and black as ever he is!)
Is as gentle as he can be.

POST CARD

Dear Aunt Katie,
    In Uganda I helped a
family paint splendid
    designs on the walls
        of their house.
They made me bright,
    fuzzy rings to wear
around my-- er, middle,
arms, and legs!
    Wait till you see!
Your Fancy Nephew,
    Koa Koala

UGANDA
0.70 • V•
EST AFRICAN
COMMUNITY

To Mrs. Katie Koala
In the Eucalyptus Grove
Australia, N.E. 2004

In the Treetops

THE VENNERS HAD COME all the way from Johannesburg to Kenya — to see wild animals. They could have seen them at Kruger Park, which was much nearer home.

But Mrs. Venner said no, that would never do. "We'd have to leave Peter home!" she said.

And Mr. Venner had agreed.

"He's still too little to camp out," he said. "Especially with lions all about."

So here were the Venners, all three, climbing up the stairs of the Treetops Hotel in Kenya.

Peter thought he was tired after the long trip. But once he had seen the tame baboons on the hotel roof, he wasn't tired at all.

He soon made friends with the quietest one, Minerva.

And all through tea, Charlie — her saucy son — came to Peter for bits of cake.

Suddenly, nighttime came to the jungle.

After dinner, the Venners went out to their own enclosed porch to look down on the lighted pond below the hotel.

It was there that the animals would be coming, to drink their fill.

"When will the animals come?" Peter whispered.

And just as he did, there was a great tromping of feet in the shadowy jungle.

A family of elephants — thirsty after the long, hot African day — were coming to the pond. Soon, there they stood drinking away — using their great, gray trunks for straws!

Monkeys swung down from the trees.

A warthog, snuffling and grunting, came out of the shadows and waded into the water.

And a great, antlered beast (an eland, Mr. Venner whispered) stalked out, sniffing the still night air. When all seemed safe, he signaled to his mate.

Then she, and their young eland, came out to drink with him.

All through the short African night, a parade of thirsty animals came to the pond.

A hippopotamus drank there, and small springbok tripped in to sip daintily.

Two tall, spotted giraffes, and one small giraffe, spraddled long legs and bent long necks to drink from the pond.

Then suddenly, an awesome sound was heard. It was the deep roar of a lion!

The other animals darted, or lumbered, into the thick shadows of the jungle. Only the hippopotamus stayed at the pond —and it sank down until only its nose showed above the water.

Now, padding softly, the lion came out into the clearing. After him came the lioness, and two plump, taffy-colored cubs.

"They lap like kittens!" whispered Peter.

"Some kittens!" his father laughed.

"Hush!" said Mrs. Venner.

And when everyone had hushed, the lion roared again — a most terrible ROAR-R-R!

It was his signal that he had drunk his fill, and wanted the lioness to hunt some food for him.

Obediently, she and the cubs followed him back into the shadows of the jungle.

By now, light was coming to Kenya's sky, pink-streaking its nighttime blue. Slowly at first, birds twittered their waking calls.

Starlings and chats, hornbills and shrikes, rollers and louries rose up and began calling out to greet the coming day.

Parrots screeched in the jungle trees.

What a cacophony, after the quiet night!

Above the trees a flock of vultures was circling round and ever down.

"No doubt to pick the bones of whatever animal the lions had for breakfast," Mr. Venner said. "Which reminds me, I'm getting hungry —"

"I'm not," said Mrs. Venner, who had turned slightly green at the thought of the lions — and vultures — and their breakfast.

"Why, Mildred!" chuckled her husband. "I think it was you, not Peter, who was too tender to camp in the wilds of Kruger Park!"

And since Peter was already on his way to the dining room — and practicing lion roars at that — Mr. Venner was most probably right.

Spear On—Spear Off!

THIS IS A SCARY GAME, played by older boys in the African bush country.

One boy must creep up to a sleeping rhinoceros (that great trampling and charging two-horned beast!) and place a spear ever so carefully on his great gray and leathery back.

The next boy must creep up and—just as carefully—take away the spear without waking the rhinoceros.

If he awakes — the boys climb trees and hide!

The Most Beautiful House

ONCE, IN SUMATRA, a small girl named Tati went to visit her brother and his beautiful wife Sumarti for six whole days.

She rode — all the way from Padang — in the dokkar of her uncle, with its bells jingling as his small horses trotted along.

A dokkar was needed, though not to carry Tati — small as she was. Rather, it was to remind her to be on best behavior during all of her visit.

This it did.

And when the dokkar stopped at her brother's new home, Tati needed no more reminders.

The house itself was most beautiful.

Many roofs it had, steep ones with curving eaves — and each wall was painted with strange and beautiful designs.

"It is like a great temple!" Tati whispered to her uncle, who nodded solemnly.

Then Tati's brother and his wife came out to greet them, and for a moment Tati stared at her beautiful sister-in-law.

So tall and straight she was!

And today she wore a long kabaya, prettier even than the one for her wedding. When she bent to kiss Tati, she smelled most beautifully of strange flowers and of sandalwood.

"Welcome, Little Sister," she said. "Our evening meal awaits your coming."

For the meal, a great crowd gathered.

Not only Sumarti's mother was there, but also her mother's mother. And all her daughters, and their husbands and children.

It was the custom there, Tati's brother told her, for a new wing to be added to the grandmother's house for each bride.

"We each live under our own roof," he said. "But much of the time, we are all together."

"A pleasant custom," Tati said politely.

And she ate her rice, and fish, and ripe papaya so daintily that her brother began to wonder what had changed his little sister.

He wondered more day by day.

For Tati would not play, or dance, or sing anymore.

Instead, she followed Sumarti about and watched all her ways.

"Are you homesick, Little Dragon?" her brother asked from time to time.

But no, Tati said she was not.

It was only at the very last moment of her visit that she told him what lay on her heart.

"I shall not always be so small," she said. "Nor wear school clothes and straight-cut hair. When I am grown, I want to suit a most beautiful house — like this one —

"And, oh my brother," she added, "I want to be just like Sumarti, too!"

It was just then that Sumarti came out to bid Tati goodbye. Over her arm, she carried the beautiful kabaya that she had worn on the first night of Tati's visit.

And she gave it to Tati!

"It is much too large now, Tati," she said. "But when you are *orang sarem puan*, I think it will suit you well."

"I hope that may be soon!" cried Tati.

Sumarti smiled and said, "There is time enough, Little Sister."

And her husband, Tati's big brother, laughed and said, "Yes, time enough, Little Dragon — we would keep you just as you are now."

Then up drove the dokkar of Tati's uncle. In she hopped, the kabaya in her arms. And away she rode, waving and calling her goodbyes until she was well out of sight of all who lived in that most beautiful house.

The kabaya was hers, and most beautiful. But now Tati thought it could wait — and she, too — through the many days and years until she grew to be *orang sarem puan*, and beautiful and tall, as well.

Wayang Kulit

Behind the screen,
The puppets act out
An old, old story
Told by the dalang,
As he makes them move
Through their parts.

Shadows they are
Behind the gauze —
But I can see them all,
Barong to Rangda
The evil one, and
In bright colors.

How do you do
All this, Dalang?
Have you a magic —
Or do my eyes and mind
Help make the shadows
Come to life?

POST CARD

Dear Chums and Chaps,
    This will be my
              last card!
I'm on the last lap of
   a long and smashing
        trip. We're heading
for the Indian O.,
     and then Perth in
        our own Australia.
Can't wait to see you all!

Your homesick
friend, Koa Koala

To all Chums and Chaps
% the Postmaster
Perth, Australia 2007

A Strange Flying Object

IN EARLY MARCH—the beginning of autumn in Australia—a strange flying object was seen approaching the city of Perth.

It might have caused a panic, except that it was first seen by Stevie Addison's cousin Dinah.

"It's Koa Koala!" she told her friends. And presently, the entire school was waving so joyfully that no one thought to panic.

At least in Perth.

It was different in Kalgoorlie.

"Cooie!" cried a gold miner, seeing the object. "Run for your lives, mates!"

And into the mines they all ran.

At Alice Springs, the tourists demanded that something be done.

So did the passengers on a jeep-train, tooling along from Darwin to Adelaide.

From there, a wire was sent to the capital city of Canberra, which in turn notified all major cities to be on the alert.

"I shall cable London, and ask the Queen

for advice as well," declared the head clerk. But word came back that Her Majesty was out of town.

By now, the strange flying object had alarmed a sheepman on a sheep station, a stockman on a vast cattle station, and a lyrebird strutting about in the mallee.

"A giant ostrich egg!" he screamed. "A giant ostrich will hatch, and gobble us all!"

Fortunately, Kookaboora was at hand.

"Nonsense!" he said. "It's only Koa Koala and his marvelous balloon, coming home—a great day for Australia!"

The lyrebird, looking rather annoyed, gave a faint cheer and went on strutting.

But the marvelous gas balloon had by now alarmed an aborigine of fierce mien.

He got ready to bring it down with his boomerang. Roger Morumbo, who was on a short visit to his home in the bush, quickly grabbed the lethal weapon.

And Koa was saved in the nick of time.

Unaware of any alarms, he was licking his lips at the sight of the many eucalyptus trees in his beautiful homeland.

"East, west—home's best!" he told himself, and—as Balloon was now not far from Sydney itself—he began tidying up his cluttered basket and brushing his clothes.

"Won't do to have the chaps see me land in this condition!" he said.

Then through the clouds dropped his marvelous gas balloon, and Sydney—Koa's home—at last stretched out far below!

Welcome Home, Koa Koala!

"WHATEVER IS GOING ON down there?" cried Koa Koala, as — with the gas-cock open — he was descending rapidly toward the zoo.

"Hiss-s-s-s!" replied Balloon.

Which was no answer at all to the question of why the streets of Sydney were blocked with autos, and decked with colorful bunting.

Or to why the people — waving flags and cheering — crowded the sidewalks, leaned from the windows, and even perched on the rooftops!

"No doubt the Queen is here for a visit," Koa thought. "How splendid! I have always wished to have a glimpse of her."

And indeed the Queen was there.

She sat, in a long and shining auto, directly in front of the Taronga Park Zoo. Beside her, Koa noticed — as he and his marvelous gas balloon came drifting down — sat the Prime Minister with his head bared.

A band played the national anthem.

And all Koa's friends, from Mr. Addison to the beaming Platypus, crowded about.

"Welcome home, Koa Koala!" they all called skyward. "Welcome home!"

Koa blinked his eyes as — with a last, happy hiss-s-s — Balloon made a landing.

"The goings-on are for us!" he whispered, climbed unsteadily out of the basket.

In a moment, he was bowing before the Queen herself!

"Welcome, Koa Koala," she said. "We, and the Commonwealth, honor you for your long and perilous journey."

At once, the Prime Minister shifted his seat so Koa could sit beside Her Majesty.

Quite tongue-tied he was, as the cavalcade moved slowly through Sydney. So slowly did it move (because of the cheering crowds, and the storm of confetti and serpentines) that Koa's friends were able to catch up and shake his paw — or whisper in his ear.

"There's to be a corroboree for you!" whispered the excited Kiwi.

"At the Governor General's mansion!" added Kangaroo, leaping so high with joy that he went sailing right over the official auto.

"And, Koa," whispered Platypus, "you are to be knighted — by the Queen herself!"

All this, and more, was true.

In the ballroom of the mansion, Koa's marvelous gas balloon (already inflated with exactly the right kind of gas — the lighter-than-air kind) bobbed among the chandeliers.

All the tables were spread for a splendid banquet, at which Koa dined on eucalyptus salad.

"I doubt I shall ever get enough!" he said, in an aside to the Queen.

"I can well understand that," she smiled, heaping his plate with more.

When the banquet ended, the shining floors were cleared for dancing.

Round and round waltzed Koa Koala — first with one partner, then another. From the windows, he saw that there was dancing in the streets, as well.

Then suddenly, the music stopped.

A great hush fell upon Sydney.

It was time for the great ceremony of knighthood!

Escorted by dignitaries, Koa crossed the

ballroom and knelt before the Queen.

When he arose, he was no longer simply Koa Koala from the Taronga Park Zoo.

He was Sir Koa the Traveled.

How the crowd cheered!

The official auto was soon brought round.

And Koa, on the shoulders of his friends, was carried to it and tucked in on the seat.

With his dear old friends around him, and back in his dear Down Under, Koa thought for a moment that nothing was wanting.

Then he began thinking that something — or someone — very important was missing.

"Balloon!" he cried out. "What has become of my friend Balloon?"

"Not to worry!" said Roger Morumbo, who had arrived from the bush by jet. "Balloon is precisely where he should be."

"And where is that?" demanded Koa, fearing he might never see his marvelous

—and faithful—gas balloon again.

Grinning, Wallaby pointed skywards.

So Koa Koala looked skywards.

And there, stoutly moored to the auto, was Balloon — sailing happily along under the clear, bright stars of Australia.

"We're home," sighed Koa. "And home we stay. Right, old chums and cobbers?"

"Right!" cried his friends from the zoo.

But Balloon said, "Hiss-s-s!" rather sadly.

"That's true," murmered Koa. "We did have such times with new friends all over the world!"

"Well, home we'll stay," he went on, "unless when spring comes — I just happen to get another bad case of the wanderlust."

And, "Hiss-s-s-s!" went Balloon.

Which meant — no question about it — that he (at least) was in complete agreement with his friend, Sir Koa the Traveled.

New Words from Koa Koala's Log

Egypt	91	Fellahin (fehl-uh-HEEN) are farmworkers in Egypt.
		Sakia (SAH-kee-eh) An ancient machine for carrying water to irrigation ditches
		Brazier (BRAY-zhur) A coal heater or stove made of brass
India	92	Charpoy (char-POHY) A bed with a wooden frame and woven-rope surface
		Hookah (HOOK-uh) A pipe with a big water bowl to cool the smoke
		Chirags (chihr-AHGZ) are tiny clay oil lamps.
		Dal (dahl) is a food made of small peas and is served at every meal.
		Ghee (gee) A kind of butter used in cooking
	94	Ganesh (gahn-EESH) The Hindu god in charge of all new projects.
Thailand	96	Nai Ti (NIGH-tee) means "Little Mister."
		Mai pen rai (MIGH-pehn-righ) "Never mind."
		Sum-o (SUHM-oh) is a fruit something like a grapefruit.
	97	Nung, song, sam, see, har, hok means one, two, three, four, five, six.
		Durian (door-ee-AHN) is a large, sweet fruit.
		Satangs (suh-TANGHZ) are pennies in Thailand.
		Khob khun (KAHB-koon) means "thank you."
Viet Nam	99	Hoa Binh (HOH-uh BIHN) "What is peace?"
		Tilipia (till-uh-pee-uh) are tiny fish that live in rice paddies.
Japan	106	Hai! (high) means "hello," and "yes."
		Ojii-san (oh-GEE-sahn) means Honorable Grandfather.
	107	Tatami (tu-TAHM-ee) Small rice-grass mats for the floor
Mexico	112	La suerte (lah SWAYR-tay) means luck.
		Bueno (BWAY-noh) means good.
		El patrón (ehl pah-TROHN) The boss of a crew of migrant workers
	113	Madre mia (MATH-ray MEE-uh) The exclamation, "My mother!"
		Padre (PAHTH-ray) means father.
Costa Rica	115	Beneficio (behn-eh-FEES-ee-oh) The place where coffee is processed
Puerto Rico	116	Machetes (mah-CHEH-tehs) Sharp knives for cutting sugar cane
	117	Colorín colorado (koh-lahr-EEN koh-lohr-RAH-doh) "And so the story ends."
	118	El Yunque (ehl HOONG-kay) The Anvil, the name of a flat-topped mountain
Brazil	119	Minha direita desocupada (MEEN-ah dihr-ree-EH-tuh dehs-oh-koo-PAH-dah) is the name of a game played in Brazil.
Bolivia	121	Muchos gracias (MOO-chohs GRATH-ee-uhs) "Many thanks."
Argentina	122	Grande (GRAHN-deh) means large, or grand.
		Estancia (ehs-TAHN-see-uh) A ranch house, or a ranch
	123	Mas bonitas (MAHS boh-NEE-tahs) means the prettiest.
		Gauchos (GOW-chohs) means cowboys.
	124	Magnifico (mahg-NEEF-ee-koh) means magnificent.
		Amigo (uh-MEE-goh) is a friend.
		Mate (MAH-tay) is a kind of tea.
Ghana	128	Fu-fu (foo-foo) A food made of cassava
	129	Cassava (kuh-SAH-vuh) A starchy root-vegetable grown in Africa
	130	Ashanti (uh-SHAHN-tee) are a people in Ghana.
Uganda	131	Gorilla gorilla beringei (bayr-ihng-ee) Largest of the great apes
Sumatra	134	Dokkar (doh-kahr) A horse-drawn taxi, with many jingling bells
		Kabaya (kuh-BAH-yuh) A fitted jacket—either long or short
		Orang sarem puan (oh-rang SAH-rehm poo-ahn) means a grown woman.
Indonesia	136	Wayang Kulit (way-ahn'g koo-lit) Shadow Plays using puppets
		Dalang (duh-LANG) The puppeteer for the Shadow Plays
		Barong (buh-ROHNG) The Spirit of Good, a dragon puppet
		Rangda (RANG-duh) The Spirit of Evil in the Shadow Plays
Australia	137	Cooie! (Koo-ee) is an exclamation—like an excited "hello!" or "wow!"
		Mallee (MAL-ee) Scrub eucalyptus—or a place where it grows wild
	139	Down Under is a nickname for Australia because it's below the equator.
		Cobbers are chums or best friends in Australia.

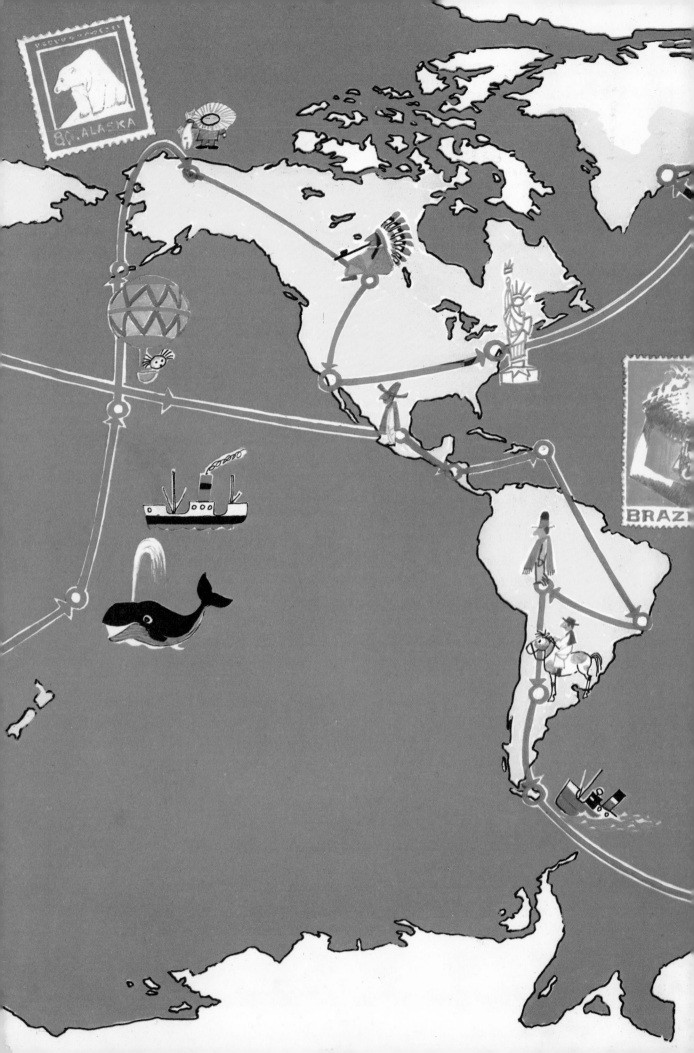